HAMLET
PRINCE OF
DENMARK

Adapted by Peggy L. Anderson & Judith D. Anderson

Cover Design by Nancy Peach

High Noon Books
A division of Academic Therapy Publications
20 Commercial Boulevard
Novato, CA 94949-6191

International Standard Book Number: 1-57128-154-1

14 13 12 11 10
12 11 10 09 08 07 06 05

Table of Contents

ABOUT
WILLIAM SHAKESPEARE
(1564-1616)

William Shakespeare was born in Stratford-upon-Avon, a market town about eighty miles northwest of London. His father was a glovemaker and a trader in wool, hides, and grain. The family, which had eight children, while not rich, led a comfortable life. William was the third child in the family, and it is thought that he attended the Stratford grammar school where classes started at six or seven in the morning and lasted until five or six in the late afternoon. When the family's finances declined, it became necessary for him to leave school to go to work for a local tradesman.

He married Anne Hathaway when he was eighteen and she was twenty-six. They had three children, including twins.

It is not known exactly when or why Shakespeare left Stratford and moved to London where he quickly became involved in the theater both as an actor and a playwright. Theaters in London were closed from 1592 to 1594 because of the terrifying plague that swept throughout Europe, so Shakespeare spent his time writing plays and publishing two long narrative poems that immediately became popular and started him on the road to fame.

We can tell from the records of the number of properties he bought in London and Stratford that his income was more than ample. His days were busy acting at the Blackfriar and Globe Theaters and writing new plays to be performed there.

Shakespeare was only fifty-two when he died in Stratford. His birthplace and Anne Hathaway's cottage have been furnished to look as much as possible as they did in Shakespeare's time and are visited by thousands of tourists and admirers each year.

To this day Shakespeare's works can be found on stages in every country in the world. The work of no other playwright has been performed in so many nations throughout so many centuries. His friend Ben Johnson wrote in 1623, "He was not of an age, but for all of time." By now we know Johnson's observation was absolutely correct!

HAMLET
PRINCE OF
DENMARK

THE STORY

Prologue

I must warn you before you begin. The tale that you are about to read is a sad one. It is also frightening. It is about murder, madness, and revenge. There is little happiness that comes to the characters within these pages. Their lives are torn apart by a chain of unhappy events. The plot twists and turns to take the reader to the darkest corners of men's souls. This is the most famous of all Shakespeare's works. And it is a story that you are not likely to ever forget.

Act I
Scene 1

Our story takes place in a castle in Denmark. This is a beautiful country with long snowy winters. On the very evening the story begins, snow was falling. It was bitterly cold. Frosty breath hung in the air among the guards who were standing watch, protecting the great castle Elsinore. They were happy to be relieved by two men assigned to take over their duty.

Marcellus, one of the guards, asked, "Well, did this *thing* appear again tonight?"

Bernardo answered, "I have seen nothing."

Marcellus spoke again. "Horatio doesn't believe us. He thinks it's all in our minds. That's why I've brought him along tonight. If he sees, he will believe."

"It will not appear," said Horatio. He rolled his eyes in disbelief.

"I'm glad you are so sure," said Bernardo. "It's easy for you to say. You refuse to listen to our story. That is because you haven't seen the ghost we've met for the last two nights."

Bernardo's words had barely left his lips when a ghostly figure appeared out of nowhere. It was as pale as the snow. A tall figure dressed for battle. The moon cast a glow on his armor. What an eerie sight! The ghost moved slowly, but steadily as if he had a purpose in mind.

The guards could not believe their eyes. They held their breath.

Finally, Bernardo spoke. "It's the dead king. It is! Isn't it?" He could not be sure. His knees were knocking. His heart was madly pounding.

"Talk to it, Horatio!" said Marcellus.

Horatio was shocked into silence. He had been so sure that the ghost story was false. But there it was. There was no denying it. He came back to reality. "Who are you?" he demanded. "What are you doing here? Why are you wearing the dead king's armor? Speak!"

But the ghost did not speak. Instead he left. It appeared as though he had floated away from the scene. The guards were frightened and confused. What had they seen?

Horatio screamed into the silent night. "Stop! Speak! I command you to speak!" But the ghost did not heed his command.

"He's gone," said Marcellus. "He won't answer you now."

Bernardo could not resist. "Well, Horatio, what's the matter? You look pale. And you are trembling. You tell us. Is this just a fantasy?"

"I wouldn't have believed it," said Horatio. "But I saw it with my own eyes." He was shaken to the core. He had not expected the ghostly sight that he had seen.

"Does it look like the king, or not?" asked Marcellus.

"It did," answered Horatio. "He had the same armor he wore to battle Norway. How strange!"

"Why would the dead king be dressed for battle?" asked Marcellus. "By day our country is preparing for war. By night our dead king appears as a ghost ready to fight. What is happening?"

"I'll tell you what I've heard," said Horatio. "You all know that the King of Norway lost his land to us. When he and old King Hamlet fought, they made a pact. Whoever lost the battle would give their land to the winner. King Fortinbras of Norway was the loser. Our king won the battle and the land. Now I've heard that Fortinbras' son is getting ready to take back the land his father lost. Could it be that the ghost is a warning sign? It might be a bad omen."

These words had barely left Horatio's lips when the ghost came back. He seemed to know they were talking about him. The pale figure floated slowly by the men. But the spirit still said nothing.

Horatio could not stay silent. "If you can use your voice, speak to me! Are you here to warn us? Is something going to happen to our country?"

The ghost seemed as if he would speak. Yet, at that moment a cock crowed. And once again the spirit figure started to leave.

Marcellus was frantic. He yelled, "Should I strike him with my spear?"

"Yes, if he won't stay!" said Horatio. His eyes searched for the ghost.

Bernardo cried out, "There he is!"

"He's over here," said Horatio. But the figure moved out of sight.

"He's gone!" said Marcellus. The ghost had vanished again.

"It was about to speak when the cock crowed," said Bernardo.

"He seemed to be startled by the sound as if he were guilty," said Horatio.

"The ghost faded on the crowing of the cock," said Marcellus. "I've heard it said that during the Christmas season, the cock's crowing protects us from evil."

"I've heard that, too. And now I believe it," said Horatio. "We had better tell young Hamlet about this. This spirit will surely speak to him. Isn't it our duty to tell him?"

Marcellus agreed. "Let's tell him. I know where we can find him this morning." And the men quickly left. They were eager to share this experience with the dead king's son.

Act I
Scene 2

Inside the castle, the king and his queen entered the great stateroom. Many other members of the court followed. It was a warm inviting room. Several large fireplaces were roaring. Deep red carpeting flowed through the room like a royal river. Gold and burgundy brocade hung from the windows like a majestic waterfall. Masses of glittering candles cast a soft glow throughout.

King Claudius was a large handsome man with more gray than blonde hair. His heavy moustache and beard were silver. He was a cheerful man with smiling blue eyes. His queen, Gertrude, was even more attractive than her husband. She was tall and slim with a crown of softly curling blond hair that hung to her waist. Her skin was clear and naturally tinted with pink like a china doll. Gertrude seemed to light up the great hall as she made her royal entry.

Claudius had recently taken the throne as a result of his brother's sudden death. King Hamlet had been the beloved ruler of Denmark until two months ago. Claudius also took something besides the crown. He took his brother's wife. This had caused something of a stir at court. Although the new king was given permission to wed Gertrude, it did not seem right to many people. Some said that it was against the rules of the church. Others said that it happened too quickly. Prince Hamlet, the old king's son, was particularly opposed to the union.

Claudius told the court that he missed his brother sorely. Yet he didn't show it. He seemed happier than he had ever been in his life. In fact, people around him commented on how joyful he appeared to be. Claudius didn't want the court to gossip about his marriage. He was trying to put an end to these rumors.

"My grief is great for the loss of my brother," Claudius said. "The whole kingdom mourns for him. But we must go on. Therefore, it is with both sorrow and joy that I married my sister-in-law. Our enemies believe that the king's death has caused us to be weak. Young Fortinbras of Norway has threatened us. I must show him that Denmark is stronger than ever. I have sent a letter to his uncle today. I have demanded that his nephew's attack be stopped. We won our lands fairly. We will not lose them to anyone!"

Claudius was confident that the letter would stop the young Fortinbras. He now turned his attention to the court. Looking at a young man, he said, "Laertes, what is new with you?"

"I came home from France for your coronation. Now I would like to ask permission to return," said Laertes as he bowed to the king.

"What does your father say?" said Claudius, referring to Polonius.

"He has agreed to let me return," answered Laertes.

"Well, then, I also agree. Go with my grace." The king turned to another young man at court. This man had very fair coloring. He resembled Claudius. "My nephew Hamlet, now my son...."

This young man turned away. It was easy to see that he disliked the king. Under his breath, he said, "You may be my kin, but you are not kind."

"How is it that the clouds still hang over you?"

asked Claudius.

"That's not so," replied Hamlet. "I'm too much in the sun."

His mother, Queen Gertrude, spoke gently to him. "Good Hamlet, cast off your mourning. Your father was a noble man. But he's gone now, as all lives must end. He is in eternity."

"Yes, it is common to die," said Hamlet. Claudius and Gertrude did not share his great sorrow.

"If you know this, then why does it seem to bother you so much?" asked his mother.

"*Seems?* I don't know what *seems*, Mother. But I know what is!" Hamlet could not believe that his mother was so unfeeling. After all, it was *her* husband who had died. "I am sad because I have lost my father. Nothing can change that."

At this point, Claudius interrupted. "Hamlet, you have a sweet and good nature. It is right that you should be sad about your father. But you must understand that your father lost his father. And his father before lost his father. The son who is left behind must go on. To continue your sorrow is to be stubborn. It is an unmanly kind of grief."

The king's words stung Hamlet's ears. What nerve he had! How could he say that grief was unmanly?

Claudius continued to speak to Hamlet about his behavior. "You must understand. You are next in line for the throne. Throw off this grief. Think of us. You cannot go back to school in Wittenburg. You must stay here and and assume your rightful place at court."

"Please, Hamlet, don't go," begged his mother. "I pray that you'll stay with us."

"I'll obey you, Mother," said Hamlet stiffly.

"Hamlet, you are a good and loving son," said the king. "I'm pleased. Your answer makes my heart smile.

Let's drink a toast! I'll fire the cannons! Come, let's go."

With that, the new king led everyone out of the room. They were going to celebrate. Only one person stayed behind. Hamlet, the old king's son.

He hung his head and thought about his father. Hamlet was so sad he wished he were dead. "Oh, that this too, too solid flesh would melt," he whispered to himself. He wanted to kill himself, but he could not. He would never do that. It was a sin to take one's life. Hamlet was distraught and depressed. He could not stop thinking about how life had changed greatly in the last two months.

Hamlet wondered how his mother could change so quickly. In the past, she had clung to his father, refusing to let him go for a minute. And then within a month of his father's death, she was clinging to another man in the same way. "Frailty thy name is woman," Hamlet said out loud. "She couldn't wait to marry another man...my father's brother!" He felt as if his heart were shattered. "But I must hold my tongue," he cried out softly. Hamlet felt so alone in his grief.

Hamlet's thoughts of his father were interrupted by the sound of hurried footsteps in the hall. Horatio, Marcellus, and Bernardo entered the stateroom. Hamlet greeted them as if nothing were wrong. In spite of his sorrow, he was particularly glad to see Horatio, who was a fellow student at the university.

"Horatio, what brings you here from Wittenburg?" Hamlet asked. Horatio told him that he had come to Elsinore for King Hamlet's funeral. Hamlet didn't believe him. "Don't mock me. You came for my mother's wedding."

"It did follow rather quickly," said Horatio.

"Thrift, thrift, Horatio. The funeral meats were needed for the wedding feast," said Hamlet. It was obvious that he was being sarcastic.

"My lord," said Horatio, "I think we have seen your father."

"Seen who?" said Hamlet, disbelieving what he had heard.

"We think we saw the king, your father!" repeated Horatio.

"The king, my father?" said Hamlet.

Horatio told him the story. "For two nights Marcellus and Bernardo saw a spirit who looked like your father. They were standing watch when they saw this ghost who was fully dressed in a suit of armor. They were struck with great fear at this sight. They swore me to secrecy. On the third night, I kept watch with them. And when I saw the ghost, I knew it was your father."

"Was this figure armed?" asked Hamlet.

Marcellus and Bernardo answered at the same time. "From head to toe!"

"How did he look?" asked Hamlet.

"He seemd more sad than angry," said Horatio.

"What was his beard like?" said Hamlet.

"Just as it was in life, streaked with silver," answered Horatio.

"I will come with you tonight. Perhaps he will come again," said Hamlet eagerly. His mind raced with thoughts. Could that really be his father?

"To your honor," shouted the three men as they left Hamlet.

Alone with his thoughts, Hamlet tried to understand the meaning of his friends' report. "All is not well," he said to himself. Something was dreadfully wrong. He wished the night would hurry. Be patient, he thought, as he looked to the sky for a welcome darkening.

Act I
Scene 3

Laertes and his sister, Ophelia, were visiting in their apartment in the castle. Ophelia was a beautiful young woman. While her brother had dark hair, hers was golden with a red tint. Her blue-green eyes sparkled when she spoke. Ophelia was a gentle young girl who was good and kind. Some said that she was too trusting of others. But that quality was also part of her charm.

Her brother had just finished telling her that he must leave soon. Ophelia and her brother were very close. She had confided in him that Hamlet was in love with her. Laertes didn't believe it.

"Hamlet is trifling with you. This love is like perfume. It is something very sweet that lasts no more than a minute," Laeartes said.

Sweet Ophelia couldn't believe that was true. "Nothing more than that?" she asked softly. The very thought of it caused her to tremble. She believed in Hamlet's love.

"Think of it as nothing more," he said. "Perhaps he loves you now, but his will is not his own. He is a prince and must marry one of royal blood. Do not lose your honor to him," warned her brother.

"I'll take your words to heart," said Ophelia. She wondered if her brother was right.

Their father, Polonius, had heard them talking. "Are you still here, Laertes?" he asked. Laertes was supposed to have left for France over an hour ago. "You should have gone abroad by now. But as long as you are still here, I have some advice to give you."

Laertes and Ophelia exchanged knowing glances. Their father was known for being long-winded.

"Give every man your ear," Polonius said, "but none your opinion. Dress well, but not too fancy. Neither a borrower nor a lender be. And above all, to thine own self be true." He continued to offer his advice on all things. As he talked more, Laertes and Ophelia listened less.

Finally Polonius finished, and Laertes said good-bye to his family. "Ophelia, don't forget what I have said to you," Laertes said.

"I won't. It's locked in my memory, and you shall keep the key," she said.

When Laertes was gone, Polonius questioned his daughter about those parting words. "What is it that he said to you, Ophelia?" he asked. Ophelia was forced to confess that Hamlet had been the subject of their conversation. Her father thought as much. "Lately I have heard that you are spending much time with him. What is between the two of you? Give me the truth."

"He has spoken of his affection for me," she said in a low voice that her father could barely hear.

"Affection!" said Polonius. "And do you believe him?"

"I do not know what I should think," she said, lowering her head.

"Well, I will tell you what to think!" he said sternly. Polonius was not at all pleased with his daughter's words. "Hamlet is a young man with burning blood. Do not believe him. From this time on, do not see him or talk to him. Do you understand?"

"Yes, my lord, I shall obey," Ophelia said with a heavy heart.

Act I
Scene 4

As Polonius was advising his daughter, Hamlet and his friends were heading for the watchtower. "What time is it?" asked Hamlet.

"Not yet twelve," said Horatio. "It is about the time when we saw the ghost arrive last night. Look! Here he comes!"

The ghost moved slowly toward the three men.

"Angels above!" cried Hamlet. "Father, King of the Danes, why have you come back from the grave?"

The ghost gestured for Hamlet to come with him.

"He wants me to follow," said Hamlet.

"No, don't!" cautioned Horatio. "He might lead you to your death."

"Don't interfere or I will make *you* into a ghost," answered Hamlet. "Stay away!" He was determined to get to the bottom of this mystery.

His friends watched anxiously as Hamlet followed the ghostly figure. They could not let Hamlet disappear into the night with this spirit. "Let's follow them," suggested Marcellus. "For his safety, we cannot obey Hamlet."

"Yes, we must find out what is happening," said Horatio.

"Something is rotten in the State of Denmark," answered Marcellus. "We will find out what it is."

Act I
Scene 5

Horatio and Marcellus followed their young prince and the ghostly figure. They were careful not to be seen. They heard Hamlet begging the ghost to speak. And finally he did. In a solemn voice, the ghost began to tell his story.

"Listen carefully to what I say. I am your father's spirit. You must seek revenge for his unnatural murder," said the ghost.

"Murder!" said Hamlet. Although he had great surprise in his voice, there was less in his heart. His suspicions were now confirmed.

"Murder most foul," said the ghost.

"Tell me quickly so I may make plans for revenge!" cried Hamlet.

His father's ghost explained how Claudius, his own brother, had poured a deadly poison in his ear while he had been sleeping in the orchard. This poison went quickly into his bloodstream and killed him in minutes. The spirit explained that Claudius committed the murder to win the hand of Gertrude in marriage. He desired her so much that he was willing to kill his brother for her.

As Hamlet listened to the ghost's story, anger grew inside him. The confirmation that his uncle had truly murdered his father left him trembling with rage. He vowed to give up everything in his life to avenge this deed. From this time forward, he would be single-minded in his pursuit of justice. His uncle must pay for this terrible crime. Hamlet swore to follow through with this plan.

When Horatio and Marcellus felt that they could make themselves known, they called out to Hamlet. He told them that they must not tell anyone of the ghost they had seen tonight. They both agreed to silence. But that wasn't good enough for Hamlet. He made them swear on their swords. When the ghost came back and issued the same order, Horatio and Marcellus quickly agreed. They swore again to keep the secret.

Act II
Scene I

In one of the staterooms in the castle, Polonius was talking to another man, Reynaldo, about engaging him to spy on Laertes in France. Polonius didn't really trust his son. He talked on and on, often forgetting his train of thought as he rambled about the importance of a father's knowing everything about his son. As Polonius said good-bye to Reynaldo, a breathless Ophelia ran into the stateroom.

"Father, I've been so frightened," she cried.

"By what?" said Polonius.

"As I was sewing in my room, Hamlet burst in with his shirt open, his stockings pulled down to his ankles, and no hat on his head," said Ophelia.

"Is he mad for your love?" asked Polonius.

"I don't know. I fear it might be true," she said in hushed tones.

"What did he say to you?" Polonius demanded.

"He took me by my wrists and held me tightly, staring at my face for the longest time. Finally, he made this pitiful cry and let go of me. He ran out the door with his eyes fixed on me."

"Come with me," said Polonius. "We must tell the king about this. This love has caused madness. Have you said anything to Hamlet recently?"

"No, I did as you commanded," said the obedient

daughter. "I refused his letters and visits."

"That must have made him mad," said Polonius. "We must find the king."

Act II
Scene 2

As Polonius and Ophelia were searching for the king, Claudius was welcoming two of Hamlet's fellow students. He had summoned Rosencrantz and Guildenstern to Elsinore to help uncover the reason for Hamlet's strange behavior.

"Welcome!" said Claudius. "We are glad to see you here. We need you to help us. Both of you have known Hamlet since childhood. We need you to find out why he is acting so strangely. He is nothing like the young man we all knew."

"Gentlemen, Hamlet is so close to you," said Gertrude. "I know he confides in you more than anyone else. Please stay and help us. Your kindness will be repaid."

Rosencrantz and Guildenstern both agreed to do what they could for the king and his queen. As they went to look for their friend Hamlet, Polonius entered the stateroom.

"I believe I have found the cause of Hamlet's madness," said Polonius.

"Tell us quickly," said Gertrude. She wanted Polonius to get to the point.

"I will be brief. Your noble son is mad," said Polonius smugly. "He is mad with love for my daughter. Listen to this letter he wrote to her." Polonius started to read a tender love letter that Hamlet had written to Ophelia. As he read the words of love, it was clear that

27

Gertrude was surprised. Polonius finished by reading the following lines with a flourish:

Doubt thou the stars are fire,
Doubt that the sun doth move,
Doubt truth to be a liar,
But never doubt my love

Claudius had also been surprised at Hamlet's words of love. He wanted to know how Ophelia felt about Hamlet. Polonius told the king that he had ordered Ophelia to stay away from Hamlet because he was royalty and she was not. He also explained that Hamlet had become very depressed when his daughter refused to see him.

"You see," said Polonius, "Hamlet could not bear the loss of my daughter's affection. He fell into sadness. Then he stopped eating. And now he has entered into madness." It was obvious that Polonius enjoyed the attention he was getting from Claudius and Gertrude.

"Do you really think this is the cause of Hamlet's strange behavior?" asked Claudius.

"It may very well be," answered his queen.

"I know it is so. And I'll prove it to you," said Polonius. He then proposed a plan whereby they could spy on a meeting between Hamlet and Ophelia. Gertrude and Claudius agreed to the plan. They were ready to try anything to understand what was wrong with Hamlet. They left the stateroom discussing the plan to arrange a chance meeting between Ophelia and Hamlet.

As the three of them were leaving, Hamlet entered the room reading a book. He appeared to be deep in thought as his friends Rosencrantz and Guildenstern greeted him.

"Ah, my good friends! How are you?" asked Hamlet.

"We are fine," answered Rosencrantz.

"Well, you can't be that fine if you are sent to prison," remarked Hamlet.

"Prison?" asked Guildenstern.

"Denmark is a prison," explained Hamlet.

When Rosencrantz and Guildenstern protested that Denmark was not a prison, Hamlet explained that it was the worst prison of all, complete with dungeons. His friends tried to talk him out of his sadness, but Hamlet persisted that he was a miserable prisoner in this country. When Hamlet changed the subject by asking why they had come to Elsinore, his friends told him that they had come to visit him.

"Were you not sent for? Come now. Tell me the truth. I can tell by your faces that the king and queen sent for you," said Hamlet.

"It's true. We were sent for," admitted Guildenstern. He felt guilty for not telling his friend the truth from the beginning.

"I'll tell you why you were sent for," said Hamlet. "Lately, I have lost all happiness. And the king and queen want to know why. All the beauty of the world is gone for me. No man or woman can change that."

"Well, Hamlet, then perhaps we can help," offered Rosencrantz. "On the way to Elsinore, we came upon a group of actors. We invited them to the castle to play for you."

"Here they come now," said Guildenstern. A group of colorfully dressed actors were standing at the doorway.

"Welcome, gentlemen," said Hamlet with some pleasure in his voice. He was pleased to see them, for he had a plan. The wheels in his mind started turning. Hamlet was considering how the actors might play a part in his plan for revenge. He remembered a play about a murdered king. If these actors were to perform this play, he was sure that Claudius would admit his guilt.

"Good sirs," said Hamlet addressing the actors, "could you perform *The Murder of Gonzago*? It's one of my favorites."

"Yes, of course," said one of the actors.

"Would it be possible for you to insert a speech of a dozen or more lines, which I am writing for the play?" asked Hamlet.

"Yes, my lord," said the same actor.

"Very well," said a pleased Hamlet. "We'll see the play this evening. Goodnight now."

As the players departed with Rosencrantz and Guildenstern, Hamlet began to think about his plans. "Oh, what a weakling am I! The only way I can seek vengeance is by pricking the conscience of the king. But I will have my revenge. One way or another!"

Act III
Scene I

Rosencrantz and Guildenstern had reported their meeting with Hamlet to the king and queen. They were amazed that Hamlet had been so friendly to the actors. They were especially happy to hear that Hamlet was looking forward to the play to be performed at Elsinore. But in spite of this good news, the king and queen still planned to spy on Hamlet and Ophelia. Ophelia had been instructed to walk through a stateroom reading a book.

"I hear him coming now," said Polonius.

Hamlet had entered the stateroom where Polonius and Claudius were hiding behind a curtain. They eagerly listened.

Hamlet began to speak. "To be or not to be, that is the question. Whether 'tis nobler in the mind to suffer the slings and arrows of outrageous fortune or to take arms against a sea of troubles, and then by opposing, end them. To die, to sleep. To sleep. . . .perchance to dream. Ay, there's the rub. For in that sleep of death, what dreams may come? That is what makes us pause. For who among us would chose to suffer through life's pains when we could so easily end life? But for the dread of something after death. Death is, after all, an undiscovered country from whom no traveler has returned. Thus conscience makes cowards of us all."

Hamlet wondered whether he should kill himself because he was so upset over his father's murder and his own future. As Ophelia approached, he was temporarily distracted from his troubles. "The fair Ophelia, you remind me of past sins."

"Hamlet, I have some things of yours. I have wanted to return them to you. Please take them now," said Ophelia in a hushed voice. It was clear that she still loved her handsome young prince. She held out a bundle tied with a pink ribbon.

"I never gave you anything," said Hamlet.

"But, sir, you know very well you did," answered Ophelia.

"I did love you once," said Hamlet softly.

"Indeed. You made me believe you did," said Ophelia. She was on the verge of tears. It was painful for her to hear him speak of their love in the past tense.

"You should not have believed me because I did not love you," said Hamlet.

"Then I was deceived," she answered with tears falling down her cheeks.

"Get thee to a nunnery," said Hamlet in his cruelest voice. "If you do ever marry, it will be to a fool. Wise men would know that you would make monsters of them! To a nunnery, go!" With these hurtful words, Hamlet turned and left the room quickly. It was as if he hated the sight of this beautiful young girl.

The tears were now falling rapidly down Ophelia's face. She tried to wipe them away, but they were flowing too freely. She felt her heart had cracked with every insult that Hamlet hurled at her. How could this have happened?

"Oh, God, please help him!" cried Ophelia. "How could I have seen this day coming?"

At that moment Polonius and Claudius came from

behind the heavy curtain where they had been hiding.

"Love?" said Claudius. "I think not. There's something strange in his soul. I'm worried that there is some danger here. I shall send him to England. Maybe that will cure him."

"That's a good idea," agreed Polonius. "I still think that his grief was caused by Ophelia's refusal to see him. But tonight after the play, let's have Gertrude speak with him about his grief. I'll hide behind the curtains in her room. Then we will decide what is best."

"It shall be so. We must be careful," said Claudius quietly. Then he added, "Madness in great ones must not go unwatched." His concern over Hamlet's behavior was growing.

Act III
Scene 2

In the great hall of Elsinore, Hamlet was talking to the actors. They were discussing the play that would be performed. Hamlet was giving the actors tips for the performance. When everyone had arrived, the play began. *The Murder of Gonzago* was a play about a man who stole the crown and a queen. As the players spoke lines, Hamlet made comments about the characters of the play. He called attention to the part where the queen swore again and again that she would never marry if her husband, the king, died. During intermission, Hamlet asked his mother how she liked the play so far.

"The lady doth protest too much," Gertrude replied. She was referring to the queen who swore to be true to her husband.

"Oh, but I'm sure she will keep her word," answered Hamlet. Although he knew she would not. Just as his mother had not kept hers.

As the play continued, Claudius became increasingly agitated. Finally, when he watched an actor pour poison into the ear of the king, he could no longer stand it. Claudius stood up with fear in his eyes. His face had a tense look.

"What is it, my lord?" asked Gertrude. She was frightened by the fearful look on his face.

"Turn on the lights," commanded Claudius. With these words, he swiftly left the hall, leaving only the echo of his faltering footsteps. An uneasy silence hung over the great hall. One by one, all of the audience left except Hamlet. He was pleased with the outcome. The king's reaction to the play proved his guilt.

Polonius came back to the empty hall. "My lord," he said, "the queen would like to speak to you." He stood well away from Hamlet.

"Tell her I will be there by and by," answered Hamlet. He was curious. What did his mother think about the play? What did she think about the king's reaction? He would soon find out.

Act III
Scene 3

In the king's private chapel, he was praying. "Oh, my offense is rank. It smells to heaven," said Claudius with his head in his hands. The play made him understand that he would never be able to escape his crime. It weighed on his soul like lead. "How can I even ask forgiveness when I still have the crown and the queen? These are the very things for which I murdered by brother. Oh, wretched state!" he cried.

Hamlet, on his way to his mother's room, had slipped into the king's chapel. As he watched him praying, he pulled his sword from his belt. He felt an impulse to kill Claudius. But he realized he could not. For if he killed him in prayer, Claudius would go to heaven. Hamlet decided to wait until he was in a drunken sleep or in bed with the queen. Then he could have his revenge, and Claudius would surely go to hell.

Act III
Scene 4

Polonius had arrived in Gertrude's room before Hamlet. "He's coming. Remember to tell him that his pranks must stop. I'll hide here behind the curtain," he said as he quickly found a place for himself.

"Mother! Mother!" cried Hamlet. "What is the matter?"

"Hamlet, you have deeply offended your father," said Gertrude.

"Mother, you are the one who has offended my father," said Hamlet.

"Come, come, you answer with an idle tongue," said Gertrude.

"You question with a wicked tongue," replied Hamlet.

"Have you forgotten that I am your mother?" asked Gertrude.

"No, you are the queen, your husband's brother's wife," said Hamlet. "And you are my mother, but I wish it were not so."

"What are you going to do? Murder me?" asked Gertrude.

When Polonius heard these words, he became fearful for Gertrude. He started to call for help from behind the curtain. This startled Hamlet who drew his sword.

"What's this--- a rat? A rat!" Hamlet cried out striking wildly at the curtain.

"Oh, I am slain," called out Polonius. He had been fatally wounded by Hamlet's sword.

"Who was that?" asked Hamlet. "The king?" He secretly hoped that it was.

"What a bloody deed this is!" cried Gertrude. She could not believe that her son had done this.

"A bloody deed?" asked Hamlet. "It's almost as bad as killing a king and marrying his brother."

"Kill a king?" said Gertrude. What was he talking about?

Hamlet pulled two small pictures out of his shirt. "Look at these pictures. Here was your husband. And here is your new husband. Can you tell them apart? No, you apparently cannot. You can hardly blame love, because at your age, you should be able to control your passion. You should be ashamed of yourself!"

"Oh, Hamlet, say no more!"cried Gertrude. "You have turned my eyes to my soul. I see black spots there."

Suddenly a ghostly figure entered the room. It was the ghost of the dead king. He was here in his wife's room.

"Do not forget your mission," said the ghost directly to Hamlet. "Comfort your mother, Hamlet. She is weak."

"Oh, Mother, look at him!" cried Hamlet referring to the ghost. "He is so pale."

But Gertrude could not see the ghost. He was appearing for Hamlet's eyes only. Because Gertrude could not see anything, she thought Hamlet was showing his madness.

"Who are you talking about?" she asked.

"Do you see nothing?" he replied.

"Nothing at all," she said.

Hamlet watched as his father's spirit slowly slipped out of the room. He turned to his mother, "Mother, I am not mad. For the love of grace, confess your sins. Repent what you have done in the past. Don't make it worse by continuing your sins."

"Oh, Hamlet, you have cut my heart in two," Gertrude cried out.

"Do not go to my uncle's bed tonight," pleaded Hamlet. "Stop now and it will become easier to do the right thing. I'm begging you. I know I have been cruel to you. But I must be cruel only to be kind. And one more thing..."

"What shall I do?" she asked.

"Do not tell the king that I know everything or there will be trouble," he threatened.

"I won't breathe a word," promised Gertrude.

"You know I must now go to England," reminded Hamlet.

"I had forgotten," she replied.

"Yes, my so-called friends whom I trust as much as poisonous snakes are accompanying me there," he said. "I'm going to take this fool's body with me as I leave. Goodnight, Mother."

Hamlet awkwardly dragged the body down the hall as Gertrude watched in horror. She was now even more frightened of her son.

Act IV
Scene 1

Claudius had made his way to his wife's room. He opened the door cautiously. He looked around and asked, "Where is your son?" He was clearly worried.

"Lord, you can't believe what I have seen tonight," said Gertrude.

"What, Gertrude? How is Hamlet?" he asked.

"He is mad as the sea and wind when they are fighting to prove their strength. When he heard something stir from behind the curtains, he pulled out his sword and yelled, 'a rat, a rat!' He killed the good old man Polonius who was standing behind the curtain!" said Gertrude.

"Oh, my," said the king. He sat down, "As long as he is at liberty, he is a threat to everyone. Including you and me. Where has he gone?"

"He has taken the body with him. In his madness he is now weeping for what he has done," said Gertrude.

"Oh, Gertrude, we must ship him out of here before the sun sets today," said Claudius.

Rosencrantz and Guildenstern came into Gertrude's room. Claudius told them to find Polonius's body and bring it into the chapel. Then he told Gertrude to come with him. They would need to confide in their friends what had happened. Claudius felt that they must do this to avoid court gossip. What would everyone think about this terrible deed?

41

Act IV
Scene 2

Rosencrantz and Guildenstern found Hamlet in a hall of the castle. They asked him what he had done with the body. Hamlet answered in a riddle, implying he had turned it into dust. Hamlet's friends begged him to tell them where the body was so they could bring it to the chapel.

"I have nothing to say to a sponge," said Hamlet.

"Are you calling me a sponge?" asked Rosencrantz in a bewildered voice.

"You are a sponge that soaks up the king's orders and rewards. But when he is finished with you, he'll squeeze you dry," warned Hamlet.

"I don't understand you," said Rosencrantz. He was becoming increasingly frustrated with Hamlet. "You must tell us where the body is. And then you must go with us to the king."

"The body is with the king. But the king is not with the body," answered Hamlet. "The king is a thing---"

Guildenstern could no longer restrain himself. "A *thing*, my lord?" he asked.

"Of nothing. Bring him to me!" said Hamlet.

Act IV
Scene 3

Claudius was greatly distressed. He had not heard anything from Rosencrantz and Guildenstern. He wanted to punish Hamlet severely, but he was afraid to follow through with this. He understood well that Hamlet was popular with the Danish people. Sending him away seemed to be the best course of action.

Rosencrantz and Guildenstern reported to Claudius that they could not get the body away from Hamlet. This added to the king's anxiety.

"Bring Hamlet to me now," he demanded.

When Hamlet came a couple of minutes later, Claudius asked him where the body was.

"At supper," replied Hamlet.

"At supper? Where?" asked an astonished Claudius.

"Not where he eats. But where he is eaten by worms," replied Hamlet.

"Where is Polonius?" asked Claudius.

"In heaven," replied Hamlet.

"Hamlet, we dearly grieve for this deed. You must prepare yourself to leave for England," said Claudius.

"To England," replied Hamlet. "Farewell, dear Mother."

"I'm your father, Hamlet," said Claudius with exasperation.

"Mother and father is one flesh. So good-bye, Mother," said Hamlet.

Claudius told Rosencrantz and Guildenstern to

make sure that Hamlet left tonight. But he did not tell them that he had written orders to England instructing that Hamlet be executed as soon as he arrived. Claudius thought that Hamlet's death would be the answer to all of his problems.

Act IV
Scene 4

As Hamlet was making his way to the ship to leave for England, Fortinbras and his army were landing on the Danish coast. Fortinbras had sent a captain to ask Claudius for permission to pass through Denmark on the way to Poland. Fortinbras was planning to seize a portion of Poland.

Hamlet asked the captain why they were planning to fight for this patch of land that was known to be worthless. It could not even be farmed. And it provided no access to attack other countries. He commented on the futility of wars. Huge amounts of human life and money were expended for little reason.

The brief encounter with the captain seemed to depress Hamlet. He felt cowardly about his failure to take any action to avenge his father's murder and his mother's sins. The men in Fortinbras' army willingly went to their graves for nothing while he had great cause and yet could bring himself to little action. Standing on the windy coast, he vowed to think of nothing else but vengeance until this terrible injustice had been punished.

Act IV
Scene 5

At the castle, things were quickly deteriorating. Ophelia was aimlessly wandering through the halls of Elsinore in a state of madness. She was wearing a dirty frayed lace dress, singing songs of betrayed love. Gertrude and Claudius were upset when they observed this once beautiful young woman in such an untidy state. And there was more trouble brewing. Upon hearing about his father's death, Laertes was leading an angry mob of people to the castle to overthrow Claudius. He had heard that the king was involved in the death of his father.

"Oh, Gertrude," sighed Claudius, "when sorrows come, they come in bunches. Your son has gone. The people are angry. Polonius is dead. Ophelia is mad. And Laertes is on his way home to avenge his father's death. Gossip tells him that I am responsible for this dastardly crime!"

A messenger was escorted into the room. He told the king and queen that a crowd of people led by Laertes had overthrown the palace guards. They were chanting, "Laertes should be king! King Laertes!" The voices started to get louder. The people were coming nearer. The thundering footsteps grew louder. And then the door broke and a crowd rushed in.

"Where is my father?" demanded Laertes.

"Dead," replied Claudius. The situation was tense. And the king was fearful.

"But not by him," said Gertrude, referring to her husband.

"How did he die?" asked Laertes. "I will have my revenge!"

"I am guiltless of your father's death. But I share your grief," said Claudius.

As this heated discussion was taking place, Ophelia slowly entered the room. She was wearing the same dirty frayed lace dress. Her hair had dirt, pieces of grass, and leaves in it. She was singing a song that made no sense.

> *They bore him bare-faced on the bier*
> *Hey non nonny, nonny, hey nonny,*
> *And in his grave rained many a tear---*
> *Farewell you well my dove.*

Laertes was struck by his sister's apparent madness. "What happened to your wits?" he cried. "Now I must really have my revenge. My father is dead, and my sister is mad."

Ophelia seemed unaware of her brother. She went about her way throwing flowers at the feet of her silent observers.

"There's rosemary. That's for remembrance," Ophelia said as she tossed the herb. "Pray you love, remember. And there are pansies. That's for thoughts. I would give you violets, but they all withered when my father died."

"This is hell itself," cried Laertes. He couldn't bear to see his sister in this state.

Ophelia turned her thoughts to her dead father. She sang,

And will he not come again?
No, no, he is dead.
Go to thy deathbed.
He will never come again.

"Dear God!" cried Laertes. "Do you see this?"

"Laertes, I share your grief. But the queen and I are not involved in this. If you find we are, I will give you our kingdom," said Claudius with conviction.

"I want to know what happened to my father," said Laertes. "I want to know how he died. I want to know why he didn't have a noble funeral. I will have the answers to my questions."

"You have my word. The axe will fall where the offense is found," said Claudius solemnly.

Act IV
Scene 6

While Claudius was pledging his assistance to Laertes, Horatio had been reading a letter delivered by two sailors.

Horatio,

We were two days at sea when a pirate ship attacked us. I ended up on their ship. I made a deal with them. I promised to reward them if they would deliver these letters. I have much to tell you. You will be very surprised to hear my story.

When you have read this letter, send these men on to the king. They have letters for him. After they deliver the letters, they will bring you to me. Rosencrantz and Guildenstern are still on their way to England. I have much to tell you of them, also.

Your friend,
Hamlet

This turn of events surprised and puzzled Horatio who was eager to see Hamlet. He wanted to hear what had happened. Horatio immediately took the sailors to the king. He then asked to be led to Hamlet.

Act IV
Scene 7

As Horatio was speaking to the sailors, Claudius was following through with his plan to win Laertes' confidence. He told him that Hamlet had killed his father and had plotted to kill the king also.

"I know that I should have punished him severely, but I could not," said Claudius. "I could not punish him for the sake of his mother. She is the star in my life. And the people have great affection for him, and would not allow punishment, regardless of his faults."

"I have lost a noble father," replied Laertes. "My sister has been driven mad. I will have my revenge."

Their conversation was interrupted by the messenger who brought two letters. One was for Claudius. And the other was for Gertrude.

Claudius read Hamlet's letter out loud to Laertes. Hamlet said that he would return tomorrow. At that time he would explain to the king how he happened to return to Denmark. Laertes listened intently to this message. He welcomed the opportunity to face Hamlet. This would give him his chance for revenge!

When Claudius had finished reading Hamlet's words, he began to think of a plan. A plan that would serve his purpose as well as that of Laertes. He decided that he would make sure that Laertes had his revenge.

"Laertes," Claudius began, "was your father dear to you? Or are you like a painting of sorrow? A face without a heart?"

"Why do you ask this?" asked Laertes. He was irritated to have his sincerity questioned.

"Not that I think you did not love your father, but I know that time helps to heal." Claudius was leading Laertes. "If Hamlet comes back, what would you do to show that you are indeed your father's son?"

"I would cut his throat in church," said Laertes quickly.

"Revenge should have no bounds," said Claudius, "but perhaps there could be another way. When Hamlet returns, why don't you challenge him to a duel? And then we will make sure that only one sword point is sharpened. Yours, of course."

"I'll do it," said Laertes, "and I'll do better. I have some deadly poison that I brought with me from France. I'll dip my sword point in it. If I scratch him slightly, it will be death!"

"Let me think further of this," said Claudius. "Just in case this should fail, we need a second plan." He appeared to be deep in thought. "I have it!" he shouted. "Should he need a break in the fighting, he might call for a drink. If that happens, I'll give him a cup of wine with poison in it!"

This conversation was interrupted when his beloved Gertrude entered. She was visibly upset.

"One woe quickly follows another," she said. "Laertes, your sister is drowned."

"Drowned?" Laertes cried. "Where?"

"She was climbing a willow tree down by the brook," replied Gertrude. "She was trying to hang a garland of flowers on the tree. A limb broke and she fell into the brook. She was pulled to a muddy death."

"Ophelia has had too much water," said Laertes sorrowfully. "I forbid my tears to fall. But I don't think I can stop them. It is nature's way. These tears will put out the fires of my rage." With shoulders heaving and much loud weeping, Laertes left Gertrude and Claudius.

"Let's follow him, Gertrude," suggested Claudius. "I had just calmed him down. Now I fear his rage will start again." How deceitful he was. In fact, Claudius had just spent considerable time trying to encourage Laertes to kill Hamlet. But Gertrude didn't know anything about this. So she followed her husband, unaware that more tragedy would soon unfold.

Act V
Scene I

Two gravediggers were preparing Ophelia's grave. They were approximately halfway through with their task when one of them began to talk about the death of this young woman.

"How is it that she who killed herself will be getting a proper burial?" asked the first gravedigger. (In those times, proper burials were not given to those who committed suicide.)

"She's being buried in a Christian burial because her family's wealthy. She's surely a gentlewomen," said the second gravedigger. "If this were not so, she wouldn't have been buried here in the churchyard."

"It's the law," said the first gravedigger. "Go get me some liquor."

The second gravedigger left to find drink for his friend. As he departed, Hamlet and Horatio approached the grave. They listened to the gravedigger who was singing a love song as he worked on the grave.

"Has he no feeling for his business? How can he sing when he's making someone's grave?" asked Hamlet.

"He's so used to his work that it doesn't bother him," explained Horatio.

The gravedigger continued his work and his singing. He intently shoveled more and more dirt from the hole that would be Ophelia's resting place. In one of the shovels of dirt, he found a skull. He glanced at it briefly and then tossed it out of the grave. A few minutes later, he sent up another.

Hamlet commented on whose skulls these had been in life. He mused that one may have belonged to a lawyer, another to a man of the court, or a politician. He then asked the gravedigger whose grave was being prepared.

"A woman's, sir," he answered. "And this skull is that of a man," he said as he picked up another from the hole. "It's been in the earth for twenty-three years."

"Whose skull was it?" asked Hamlet curiously.

"It was Yorick's skull," he answered. "Yorick was the king's jester."

"Alas, poor Yorick!" said Hamlet. "I knew him well. He was a fellow of infinite jest. He carried me on his back a thousand times. He was so good to me." He held his beloved friend's skull to the light. "Oh, dear Yorick, where are your jokes and songs now?"

As Hamlet was contemplating the life of his friend Yorick, a procession of people entered and filed past him. Included in this solemn group were Claudius, Gertrude, Laertes, a priest, and several attendants carrying a coffin.

Hamlet looked up with curiosity. "Whose funeral is this?" he asked.

"Whose do you think?" said Laertes angrily.

The priest started to speak. "Although her death was questionable, we are gathered here to give her a respectable funeral."

"Is there anything more that can be done?" asked Laertes.

"There is no more to be done," answered the priest.

"From her fair and unpolluted flesh may violets spring," cried Laertes. "For my sister was an angel."

"What, the fair Ophelia?" said an astonished

Hamlet.

"Sweets to the sweet," said Gertrude. "I had hoped that you would be my Hamlet's bride. I thought I would decorate your bridal bed, not your grave," she added as she scattered flowers on the earth.

"I curse the head of the person whose wicked deed deprived me of you," said Laertes. "Hold the earth while I hold her in my arms once more." And then, quite unexpectedly, he jumped into Ophelia's grave.

Hamlet stepped forward. As Laertes climbed out of the grave, he saw him. A strangled cry escaped from his throat as Laertes lunged for his enemy. The two men struggled while the funeral attendants tried to separate them.

"Gentlemen! Gentlemen!" shouted Claudius.

"I loved Ophelia!" Hamlet shouted. "Forty thousand brothers could not love her as much as I. I would have done anything for her."

"Laertes, he is mad! I told you so," exclaimed Claudius.

"Leave him alone," said Gertrude. "All of you, let him be!"

"Do you come here to whine and cry?" Hamlet demanded. "Are you trying to outdo me by leaping into her grave? Well then, we'll both be buried with her. Let them throw a mountain of earth on us." With those parting words, Hamlet ran out of the cemetery. Horatio followed his upset friend.

"Laertes, remember what we planned," said Claudius. "Strengthen your patience."

Turning to his wife, he added, "Gertrude, you had better watch over your son." He was secretly pleased about the events he had just witnessed. There was a great deal of tension between Laertes and Hamlet. This set the stage for his other plans.

Act V
Scene 2

While Claudius was contemplating his plans for his stepson, Hamlet was telling Horatio how he had outwitted the king. Walking down the long hall to the stateroom, Hamlet explained how he had found the letter from Claudius ordering his immediate execution when he landed in England. He had written new orders that condemned Rosencrantz and Guildenstern to death. Hamlet carefully affixed the seal of the king on these papers so they would appear to be authentic.

Horatio was surprised to hear that Hamlet could so casually condemn his friends to death. "So Rosencrantz and Guildenstern went to their deaths?" he asked.

"They are not on my conscience," replied Hamlet. "They were making themselves useful to Claudius in a way that betrayed me. In the end they were betrayed themselves," he added.

Horatio had always thought of Hamlet as a quiet, sensitive person. He was having difficulty seeing his friend in this new light.

"But I am very sorry about the trouble between Laertes and myself," Hamlet said. "I'll make it up to him. It's just that his bravery in grief made me lose my temper."

Before Horatio had time to answer, a young man from the court named Osric entered the room. He told Hamlet that Claudius had made a bet regarding a sword fight between Laertes and Hamlet. This made Hamlet curious. It seemed very strange to him that Claudius would choose this moment to arrange a fight between Laertes and himself. Osric further explained that Hamlet would be the favorite in such a fight. He said that Laertes would not win three more bouts than Hamlet. Laertes wagered that he would score nine hits out of twelve. Claudius had put up six of his best horses for the bet.

"What if I refuse?" asked Hamlet.

"But, sir, you should accept the challenge," urged Osric.

"Let the swords be brought," Hamlet said. "I will try to win for him."

Osric left to tell Claudius that the duel had been arranged. Horatio, who had been listening, did not want his friend to fight. "You will lose, my lord," he cautioned.

"I do not think so," replied Hamlet. "Since Laertes has been in France, I have been in continual practice. I shall win. But I do have an uneasiness in my heart."

"If you have any doubts in your mind, listen to them," advised Horatio. "I will tell them that you are not well," he added.

Hamlet would not listen to his good friend. He insisted that he was fit for the duel. "Let it be, Horatio," he said, "for the time is right."

As they spoke, the servants were busy preparing the great hall for the duel. Containers of red wine were set on the long table. Cups of gold and silver were brought. The swords were set out for the duel. Large purple and red cushions were placed about the room for the guests. Soldiers came with trumpets and drums. There was much preparation for this event. Finally, when the great hall was ready, Claudius and Gertrude entered with Laertes.

Hamlet and Laertes shook hands. Hamlet took this moment to apologize to Laertes. "Please pardon me," he said, "for I have done you wrong. But know that Hamlet did not wrong you. It was my madness. Please be generous and forgive me."

Since Laertes was secretly planning to kill Hamlet, he did not want to alert him of this plan. So he pretended to accept the apology. The swords were then brought by Osric, who made sure that Laertes chose the one with the poisoned tip.

Hamlet and Laertes stood in fencing position. They were ready. Claudius spoke, "If Hamlet wins, I shall drink a cup of wine with a pearl thrown in. Let's begin. Judges keep a close eye."

The trumpets signaled the beginning of the duel. There was tension in the room as everyone watched quietly. Both Laertes and Hamlet were excellent swordsmen. They moved gracefully as their swords touched time and time again. Hamlet was the first to make a hit.

The king cried out, "Hamlet, the pearl is yours. Here's to your health." The trumpets blared and the drums rolled. "Give him the cup," he said excitedly. Claudius was anxious for Hamlet to drink the poisoned wine.

"Not now," said Hamlet, "I'll play this round first. Set it aside." He was focused on the duel. He was, of course, unaware of the pact that Laertes and Claudius had made for his death.

"Another hit!" cried out Hamlet as he once again touched Laertes with his sword. "What do you say?"

"I confess, it was a hit," said Laertes.

Gertrude was pleased with the duel. "The queen drinks to your fortune, Hamlet," she said. She raised the cup to her lips.

As Claudius saw her, he was gripped by fear. "Gertrude, do not drink!" he cried.

"But I must, please pardon me," she said joyfully.

Claudius watched his beloved queen drink the poisoned wine as a toast to her son's success. He felt that he was watching a nightmare unfold. The poison that he had intended for Hamlet was now killing the love of his life. His chest was tight with pain. He thought he could not bear to breathe.

"Let me wipe your face," Gertrude said lovingly to her son. Hamlet turned in her direction.

"Now is my chance to hit him," said Laertes under his breath. But he was puzzled by another feeling. "Yet, it is almost against my conscience," he thought.

Laertes was quickly brought back to the reality of the duel. Hamlet taunted him, "Come on, Laertes. This is the third bout. Give me your best!" With those words, Laertes surged forward and wounded Hamlet. They fell to the floor. Their swords fell also. They scuffled briefly. When they rose again, they had exchanged weapons. They fought on until Hamlet wounded Laertes.

Suddenly Gertrude fell. The bleeding men looked up with surprise. She cried out, "The drink! The drink! I am poisoned!"

"Who did this?" shouted Hamlet with hatred in his voice.

Laertes' conscience was again troubling him. He realized that he had also been hit with the poisoned sword point. He felt he had to tell the truth to all. "Hamlet, you are dying, too. No medicine in the world can save you. In less than half an hour we will both be dead. I am to blame. The sword point was poisoned. Your mother was also poisoned. The king is to blame!"

"The point was poisoned?" asked Hamlet softly. "Then poison do thy work." He grabbed his sword and lunged at the king, piercing him.

"Defend me!" cried the king. "I am hurt." But no one moved to help him. They all looked away. This king that they had never accepted had shown his true colors today before all.

"Drink the rest of the poison, you murderer," said Hamlet as he pressed the cup upon Claudius. "Follow my mother to the grave!" Claudius looked around one last time to see if any of his subjects would come to his aid. But they would not. Claudius slowly lifted the cup and drank the poisonous wine. Moments later he fell to the ground next to his dead queen.

"This is justice," said Laertes. "Let's exchange forgiveness. My father's death and my death are not upon you. And your death is not upon me." Before Hamlet had time to reply, Laertes fell to the floor in death.

"I am dead, Horatio," Hamlet said to his good friend.

"I will die with you," replied a pale and trembling Horatio. "There is still poison left." He stared at the sight of the bodies spread around the room. What a tragedy this had been!

"No, Horatio," said Hamlet, "if you love me, you must live to tell my story."

From far off in the distance they both heard fighting.

"What battle is this?" asked Hamlet.

Osric, who had been standing by, answered. "It is young Fortinbras, who has come from his victory in Poland."

"I will not live to see him," said Hamlet, gasping with his last breaths. "But I want it known that Fortinbras is my choice for king. In my dying voice I say it is so. Tell him what has happened here. The rest is silence." Then Hamlet fell. The prince lay dead before all.

"Good night, sweet Prince," said Horatio sorrowfully. "Angels sing thee to rest."

Loud footsteps were rushing down the hall. Fortinbras and his men appeared. "What is this?" he asked as he looked at the bodies in the great hall.

"I will tell you everything," said Horatio. "I will tell the world how these things came about. You will hear of bloody and unnatural acts. You will hear of accidents and murders. You will hear of all this and more."

"Then let us call everyone together to hear this," said Fortinbras. "It is with much sorrow that I embrace my fortune. For this is my kingdom now." Although Fortinbras was a noble leader who would gladly rule Denmark, he was sorrowful about the events that had led to his reign.

Fortinbras called his captains to carry Hamlet's body to a place of honor where his people could view him. "Carry Hamlet like a soldier," he commanded, "for had he lived, he would have proved himself most royal. He must have a soldier's funeral to speak loudly for him."

The soldiers carried Hamlet high above the crowd. His subjects followed the body with their heads bowed. There was much weeping. For the people of Denmark mourned the loss of their fair-haired prince. They had looked forward to the day that he would lead them. They had never dreamt that he would lead them in a funeral procession. The snow fell silently from a dark night that covered the young prince who would struggle no more.

HAMLET PRINCE OF DENMARK

THE PLAY

CAST OF CHARACTERS

CLAUDIUS, *King of Denmark*

GERTRUDE, *Queen of Denmark, wife of Claudius, mother of Hamlet*

HAMLET, *son of the late King, nephew of the present King*

POLONIUS, *Lord Chamberlain*

LAERTES, *son of Polonius*

OPHELIA, *daughter of Polonius*

HORATIO, *friend of Hamlet*

ROSENCRANTZ & GUILDENSTERN, *friends of Hamlet's*

OSRIC, *a courtier*

REYNALDO, *a servant to Polonius*

MARCELLUS, BERNARDO, and FRANCISCO, *officers of the guard*

FORTINBRAS, *King of Norway*

CAPTAIN

GHOST

ACTORS

PRIEST

GRAVEDIGGER I & GRAVEDIGGER II

ATTENDANTS, SERVANT, MESSENGER, SAILORS, SOLDIERS

Act I
Scene 1

Setting: The gun tower of Elsinore Castle.

(Bernardo and Francisco, two guards, enter.)

BERNARDO: Have you had a quiet guard tonight?

FRANCISCO: Not a mouse stirring.

BERNARDO: If you see Horatio and Marcellus, tell them to hurry.

FRANCISCO: I think I hear them now.

(Horatio and Marcellus enter.)

BERNARDO: Welcome, Horatio. Welcome, Marcellus.

MARCELLUS: Well, has this *thing* appeared again tonight?

BERNARDO: I have seen nothing.

MARCELLUS: Horatio says it is our fantasy. He doesn't believe us. But twice I have seen this ghost. So I have asked him to come along tonight. If the ghost appears, he will see for himself.

HORATIO: It will not appear.

(Ghost enters.)

MARCELLUS: Look! Here it comes again.

BERNARDO: It looks like the dead king.

MARCELLUS: Speak to it, Horatio.

HORATIO: Who are you? Why do you appear like the

dead king dressed for battle? I charge thee
to speak!

(Ghost exits.)

MARCELLUS: He's gone without an answer.

BERNARDO: Horatio, is not this something more than
fantasy?

HORATIO: I would not have believed it. But I saw it
with my own eyes.

MARCELLUS: Is it not like the king?

HORATIO: Yes, that was the very armor he wore in
battle with Norway. 'Tis strange.

MARCELLUS: Our country is preparing for war now.
Cannons are being bought. Ship builders
are working day and night. Who can explain
this?

HORATIO: I can. I will tell you what I have heard. Our
last king fought Norway. Our valiant King
Hamlet won many lands from Fortinbras,
ruler of Norway. Fortinbras died in that
battle. Now young Fortinbras, his son, is
trying to recover the lands lost by his father.
I think this ghost must be an omen of some
fate to come.

(Ghost enters.)

If you can use your voice, speak to me! If
you know something of our country's fate,
speak to me. Tell us so we can happily avoid
this disaster. *(Ghost walks away.)* Stay and
speak! Stop it, Marcellus!

(A cock crows.)

MARCELLUS: Shall I strike him with my spear?

HORATIO: Do it, if it will not stay.

(Ghost exits.)

BERNARDO: It was about to speak when the cock crowed.

HORATIO: Then it jumped like a guilty thing being called.

MARCELLUS: It faded on the crowing of the cock. During the Christmas season the cock is supposed to crow all night. His singing protects from the evil spirits.

HORATIO: So have I heard and do in part believe. Let us impart what we have seen tonight to young Hamlet. Upon my life, this spirit which is dumb to us will speak to him. Do you agree that it is our duty to tell him?

MARCELLUS: Yes, let us do it. I know where we can find him this morning.

(All exit.)

Act I
Scene 2

Setting: The Great Hall of Elsinore Castle.

(Claudius, King of Denmark; Gertrude, Queen of Denmark; Hamlet, Polonius, Laertes, Ophelia, and attendants enter.)

CLAUDIUS: The memory of our dear brother Hamlet's death is still green. Our hearts are grieving. The whole kingdom faces sorrow. We have been saddened by a funeral. And I have been made joyful by my new marriage. She who was my sister-in-law is now my wife. Now we must turn our attention to young Fortinbras. He is trying to win back the lands that his father lost to us. I am sending a letter to his uncle today. I told him to stop his nephew's purpose. Take this letter to him now.

(Two attendants exit with letter.)

And now, Laertes, what is the news with you?

LAERTES: I came willingly to Denmark to show my duty for your coronation. Now I must confess my thoughts are again with France. I would ask your gracious leave.

CLAUDIUS: Have you your father's permission?

POLONIUS:	At last I have agreed to let him leave. I beseech you to also give him leave to go.
CLAUDIUS:	Well then, I also agree. Go with my grace. *(He turns to Hamlet.)* My nephew Hamlet, now my son.
HAMLET:	*(Aside.)* A little more than kin, and a little less than kind.
CLAUDIUS:	How is it that the clouds still hang on you?
HAMLET:	Not so, my lord. I am too much in the sun.
GERTRUDE:	Good Hamlet, cast off your mourning. Do not forever be thinking of your father. All that lives must die. Passing through nature to eternity is common.
HAMLET:	Ay, it is common.
GERTRUDE:	If you know this, why does it seem to bother you so?
HAMLET:	*Seems,* madam? I don't know what *seems.* I know what is! My suits of solemn black are shapes of true grief.
CLAUDIUS:	'Tis your sweet nature to give these mourning duties to your father. But you must know, your father lost his father. That father lost his. The son who is left behind must go on. It is your obligation to show sorrow, but to continue shows stubbornness. 'Tis unmanly grief. You are the next in line for the throne. We ask that you not return to school in Wittenburg. Please stay with us.
GERTRUDE:	I pray thee stay with us, Hamlet.
HAMLET:	I shall obey you, madam.
CLAUDIUS:	Why, 'tis a loving and fair reply. Your gentle answer makes my heart smile. Come with

me, madam.

(All but Hamlet exit.)

HAMLET: Oh, that this too, too solid flesh would melt. That it should come to this! The King is not two months dead, not so much as two. My mother hung on him as if she loved him greatly. And yet within one month...

Frailty thy name is woman! She followed my father's body to the grave with tears. Then a month later she married my uncle. My father's brother! Even a beast would have mourned longer! She married with wicked speed. My heart is breaking, but I must hold my tongue.

(Horatio, Marcellus, and Bernardo enter.)

HORATIO: Hail to your lordship!

HAMLET: Horatio, I am very glad to see you. But what brings you from Wittenburg?

HORATIO: I came for your father's funeral.

HAMLET: Do not mock me. I think it was to see my mother's wedding.

HORATIO: Indeed, it followed quickly.

HAMLET: Thrift, thrift, Horatio. The funeral meats were needed for the marriage feast. Oh, my father. Methinks I see my father.

HORATIO: Where my lord?

HAMLET: In my mind's eye, Horatio.

HORATIO: My lord, I think I saw him last night.

HAMLET: The king, my father! Tell me.

HORATIO: For two nights Marcellus and Bernardo saw a figure that looked liked your father. They were standing watch when they saw this ghost who was fully dressed in a suit of armor. They were frightened so much they thought they would turn to jelly. I stood watch on the third night. The ghost came again. I knew it was your father.

HAMLET: You say he was armed?

HORATIO: From head to toe.

HAMLET: Did he see your face?

HORATIO: He stared at us the whole time.

HAMLET: What was his beard like?

HORATIO: It was as I have seen it in life.

HAMLET: I will watch tonight. Perhaps it will walk again.

HORATIO: I'm certain that it will.

HAMLET: I will meet you on the platform between eleven and twelve o'clock.

ALL: To your honor!

HAMLET: Mine to you. Farewell.

(All but Hamlet exit.)

HAMLET: My father's spirit, in arms! All is not well. There must be foul play. When the night comes, the foul deeds will rise.

(Hamlet exits.)

Act I
Scene 3

Setting: Polonius' apartment in Elsinore.

(Laertes and Ophelia enter.)

LAERTES: Hamlet is trifling with you. He is treating you as a toy. This is a sweet thing, but it is not permanent. It is like perfume that lasts a minute and no more.

OPHELIA: No more than that?

LAERTES: Think it no more. Perhaps he loves you now, but his will is not his own. He is royal by birth and must marry according to the benefit of Denmark. I know that you want to believe him when he says he loves you. But you must not lose your honor to him.

OPHELIA: I will take your words to heart, good brother.

(Polonius enters.)

POLONIUS: Are you still here, Laertes? You should have gone abroad by now. The wind sits in the shoulder of your sail! I will give you some advice before you leave. Give every man thy ear, but few thy voice. Listen to every man's opinion, but reserve thy judgment. Neither a borrower nor a lender be. This above all, to thine own self be true. And it must follow,

	as night into day. Thou cannot then be false to any man. Farewell, my son.
LAERTES:	Most humbly do I take my leave, my lord. Farewell, Ophelia, remember well what I have said to you.
OPHELIA:	'Tis locked in my memory. And you yourself shall keep the key.
	(Laertes exits.)
POLONIUS:	What is it that he said to you?
OPHELIA:	Something about Lord Hamlet.
POLONIUS:	Lately I have seen you with him often. What is between you? Give me the truth.
OPHELIA:	He has spoken of affection for me.
POLONIUS:	Affection! Do you believe him?
OPHELIA:	I do not know what I should think.
POLONIUS:	Well, I will tell you what to think! Hamlet is a young man with burning blood. Do not believe his vows. From this time, I do not want you to see him anymore. Do not talk with him or listen to him.
OPHELIA:	I shall obey, my lord.

Act I
Scene 4

Setting: The Gun Platform

(Hamlet, Horatio, and Marcellus enter.)

HAMLET: What is the hour now?

HORATIO: It is just before twelve. It is near to the time the spirit will walk.

(Ghost enters.)

Look, here it comes!

HAMLET: Angels defend us! Is this a good spirit or a bad one. Bring thee airs from heaven or blasts from hell? I will speak to thee. I'll call thee King Hamlet, father, royal Dane. Oh, answer me.

(Ghost gestures toward Hamlet.)

HORATIO: It wants to be alone with you.

MARCELLUS: But do not go with it.

HAMLET: It will not speak. I must follow it.

HORATIO: Do not, my lord!

HAMLET: What should I fear?

HORATIO: He might lead you to your death.

MARCELLUS: You shall not go, my lord.

HAMLET: My fate cries out. Unhand me, gentlemen! I'll make a ghost of anyone who interferes. *(To the ghost.)* Go on, I'll follow thee.

(Ghost and Hamlet exit.)

MARCELLUS: Let's follow. It is not right to obey him.

HORATIO: Yes, we must find out what will happen.

MARCELLUS: Something is rotten in the State of Denmark.

HORATIO: And we will find out what it is.

(All exit.)

Act I
Scene 5

Setting: The walls of Elsinore Castle.

(Hamlet and the ghost enter.)

HAMLET: Where are you leading me? Speak, or I'll go no further.

GHOST: I am thy father's spirit. If thou didst ever love thy dear father, revenge his foul and most unnatural murder.

HAMLET: Murder?

GHOST: Murder most foul.

HAMLET: Tell me with haste so I may sweep to revenge.

GHOST: Now, Hamlet, listen. I was sleeping in my orchard when a serpent stung me. That serpent now wears thy father's crown.

HAMLET: My uncle?

GHOST: Ay, he wanted my queen. I'll be brief. I was sleeping in my orchard as was my custom in the afternoon. Your uncle came to me and poured hebenon in my ear. This poison works as swift as quicksilver through the blood. My life, my crown, and my queen were taken by my brother's hand. Oh horrible, horrible, most horrible! Pursue the act of revenge. But do not contrive against thy mother. Leave her to heaven and to the thorns in her conscience that prick and sting her. Adieu, adieu, adieu. Remember me.

HAMLET: Remember thee? Yes, from the table of my memory, I'll wipe away all trivial records. Only your commandment shall live. I have sworn it.

(Horatio and Marcellus enter.)

HORATIO: What happened, my lord?

HAMLET: You must never tell what you have seen tonight.

HORATIO and MARCELLUS: My lord, we will not.

HAMLET: Swear it!

HORATIO: In faith, I will not.

MARCELLUS: Nor I.

HAMLET: Swear upon my sword.

MARCELLUS: We have sworn already.

(Voice under stage.)

GHOST: Swear!

HAMLET: Did you hear that?

GHOST: Swear!

HAMLET: Come here, gentlemen. Never speak of what you have seen. Swear by my sword.

(Marcellus and Horatio, heads bowed, lay their hands on the sword.)

GHOST: Swear!

HAMLET: Rest now, spirit. Let us go together with your fingers still on your lips. Oh cursed spite, that ever I was born to set it right.

(All exit.)

Act II
Scene 1

Setting: A stateroom in Elsinore.

(Polonius and Reynaldo enter.)

POLONIUS: Give him this money, Reynaldo.

REYNALDO: I will, my lord.

POLONIUS: But before you visit him, make inquiries of his behavior.

REYNALDO: I intend to.

POLONIUS: Find out what kind of company my son is keeping.

REYNALDO: Very well, my lord.

POLONIUS: I want to know what kind of youthful liberties he is taking.

REYNALDO: Such as gambling.

POLONIUS: Drinking, fencing, swearing, quarreling.

REYNALDO: Very good, my lord.

POLONIUS: Farewell.

(Reynaldo exits.)

(Ophelia enters.)

OPHELIA: Oh, my lord, my lord, I have been so frightened.

POLONIUS: With what?

OPHELIA:	I was sewing in my closet when Hamlet came in. His shirt was open. No hat upon his head. His stockings had fallen to his ankles. He was pale as his shirt and his knees were knocking together. He looked as if he had been let out of hell.
POLONIUS:	Is he mad for your love?
OPHELIA:	My lord, I do not know. But I fear it is so.
POLONIUS:	What said he?
OPHELIA:	He took me by the wrist and held me hard. He stared at my face for the longest time. Then he let out a pitiful sigh that seemed to shatter his body. He ran out the door with his eyes still on me all the while.
POLONIUS:	Come, go with me. I will go seek the king. This is love that causes desperation. Have you said anything to him lately?
OPHELIA:	No, my good lord. As you did command, I would not accept his letters, and I would not see him.
POLONIUS:	That hath made him mad. We must tell the king. This must be known.
	(All exit.)

Act II
Scene 2

Setting: The great hall of Elsinore.

(King, Queen, Rosencrantz, Guildenstern, and attendants enter.)

CLAUDIUS: Welcome, dear Rosencrantz and Guildenstern! We did long to see you. We need you to help us. Have you heard of Hamlet's strange behavior? It must be more than his father's death that has made him change so. Both of you have known him since youth. Please find out what is afflicting him. Once we know, we can help him.

GERTRUDE: Good gentlemen, he hath talked much of you. And I am sure that there are no two men living to whom he is closer. Spend time with us here and your visit shall receive a royal reward.

ROSENCRANTZ: Both your majesties, we are at your command.

GUILDENSTERN: We lay our service freely at your feet.

CLAUDIUS: Thanks, Rosencrantz and gentle Guildenstern.

GERTRUDE: And I ask you to instantly visit our changed son. Some of you, please bring these gentlemen to Hamlet.

(Rosencrantz and Guildenstern exit with servants.)

(Polonius enters.)

POLONIUS: I have found the very cause of Hamlet's madness.

CLAUDIUS: Speak of that. I long to hear.

GERTRUDE: I doubt it is no other than his father's death and our hasty marriage.

POLONIUS: Why day is day. Night is night. And time is time. Nothing but to waste night, day, and time. Therefore, since brevity is the soul of wit, I will be brief. Your noble son is mad.

GERTRUDE: Get on with it.

POLONIUS: I have a daughter who in her duty and obedience hath given me this. *(Shows letter, then reads it.)*

> *Doubt thou the stars are fire,*
> *Doubt that the sun doth move,*
> *Doubt truth to be a liar,*
> *But never doubt my love.*

GERTRUDE: This came from Hamlet?

CLAUDIUS: How hath she received his love?

POLONIUS: I told my daughter, 'Lord Hamlet is a prince out of thy star. This must not be.' I told her not to see him or accept messages or gifts. She has taken my advice. And he, when repulsed, fell into a sadness. And then into the madness wherein now he raves.

CLAUDIUS: Do you think 'tis true?

GERTRUDE: It may be.

POLONIUS:	I say positively 'tis so.
CLAUDIUS:	How can we find out for certain?
POLONIUS:	You know sometimes he walks for hours in the stateroom.
GERTRUDE:	So he does indeed.
POLONIUS:	I will send my daughter to him. We can hide behind the drapes. We can tell from the encounter if he loves her.
CLAUDIUS:	We will try it.
	(Hamlet enters, reading a book.)
	(Claudius, Gertrude, Polonius, and attendants exit.)
	(Rosencrantz and Guildenstern enter.)
HAMLET:	My excellent friends! Good lads, how do you both? What have you done to be sent to prison?
GUILDENSTERN:	Prison, my lord?
HAMLET:	Denmark's a prison.
ROSENCRANTZ:	Then the world is one.
HAMLET:	Denmark is the worst.
ROSENCRANTZ:	We think not, my lord.
HAMLET:	What brings you to Elsinore?
ROSENCRANTZ:	To visit you, my lord — no other occasion.
HAMLET:	Were you not sent for? Tell me the truth?
GUILDENSTERN:	What should we say?
HAMLET:	The truth. There is a kind of confession in your looks. I know the good king and queen sent for you.
GUILDENSTERN:	Ay, we were sent for.
HAMLET:	I will tell you why. Lately, I have lost all my

85

happiness. All the beauty of the world is gone for me.

ROSENCRANTZ: Perhaps we can help. On the way to Elsinore, we came upon a group of actors. They are coming to offer you service.

GUILDENSTERN: Here they come now.

(Acting troupe enters.)

HAMLET: Gentlemen, you are welcome to Elsinore. Can you play *The Murder of Gonzago*?

ACTOR: Ay, my lord.

HAMLET: Could you insert a speech of twelve to sixteen lines that I have written?

ACTOR: Ay, my lord.

HAMLET: Very well. My good friends, we'll see the play this evening. Until then...

(Actors, Rosencrantz, and Guildenstern exit.)

These actors will perform a play that resembles the murder of my father before my uncle. I'll observe his looks. The play's the thing wherein I'll catch the conscience of the king.

Act III
Scene 1

Setting: The great hall of Elsinore.

(King, Queen, Polonius, Rosencrantz, Guildenstern, and attendants enter.)

CLAUDIUS: Did he tell you anything about his confusion and lunacy?

ROSENCRANTZ: He does confess he feels distracted. But he does not say the cause.

GERTRUDE: Did he receive you well?

ROSENCRANTZ: Most like a gentleman. I told him about a group of actors we had met on the road. They were on the way to Elsinore. He seemed to be joyful to hear of this. Tonight they will play for him.

POLONIUS: 'Tis true. He asked me to entreat the king and queen to see the play.

CLAUDIUS: With all my heart, it doth content me much to hear this. Good gentlemen, encourage me on to these delights.

ROSENCRANTZ: We shall, my lord.

(Rosencrantz and Guildenstern exit.)

CLAUDIUS: Sweet Gertrude, leave us, too. We have arranged for Ophelia and Hamlet to accidentally meet. Her father and I will spy on them. From their encounter we may judge if he suffers from affliction of love or not.

GERTRUDE: I will obey you.

(Gertrude and attendants exit.)

(Ophelia enters.)

POLONIUS: Ophelia, walk here. Read this book. This exercise will show your loneliness. I hear him coming!

(Polonius and Claudius exit.)

(Hamlet enters.)

HAMLET: To be or not to be. That is the question. Whether 'tis nobler in the mind to suffer the slings and arrows of outrageous fortune, or to take arms against a sea of troubles, and by opposing, end them. To die, to sleep — no more. And by a sleep to say we end a thousand natural shocks that flesh is heir to. 'Tis a consummation devoutly to be wished. To die, to sleep — to sleep, perchance to dream. Ay, there's the rub, For in that sleep of death what dreams may come, when we have shuffled off this mortal coil, must give us pause. For who among us would suffer through life when it could so easily be ended? But for the dread of something after death. Death — the undiscovered country, from which no traveler ever returns. Thus, conscience makes cowards of us all. *(To Ophelia.)* The fair Ophelia, be all my sins remembered.

OPHELIA: How does your honor?

HAMLET: Well, thank you.

OPHELIA:	My lord, I have some things of yours that I that I have longed to return. I pray you receive them now. *(Holds out a bundle tied with ribbon.)*
HAMLET:	I never gave you anything.
OPHELIA:	My lord, you know right well you did. And with them words of so sweet breath as to make the things richer. But now their perfume is lost. Take these again, for rich gifts become poor when givers prove unkind.
HAMLET:	I did love you once.
OPHELIA:	Indeed, my lord, you made me believe so.
HAMLET:	You should not have believed me. I loved you not!
OPHELIA:	I was the more deceived.
HAMLET:	Get thee to a nunnery. Why would you be a breeder of sinners? It would have been better if my mother had never borne me.
OPHELIA:	Oh help him, sweet heavens!
HAMLET:	Get thee to a nunnery, go. Farewell. Or if thou will marry, marry a fool. For wise men know well enough what monsters you make of them. To a nunnery, go!
	(Hamlet exits.)
OPHELIA:	Oh, woe is me to see what I have seen.
	(Claudius and Polonius enter.)
CLAUDIUS:	Love? His affections do not tend that way. There is something in his soul that is causing the melancholy. I am afraid he might do something dangerous. I must send him to England with speed.

POLONIUS: I agree. But yet I do believe that the origin of his grief sprung from neglected love. *(To Ophelia.)* Ophelia, you need not tell us what Hamlet said. We heard it all. *(To Claudius.)* My lord, after the play, let the queen talk to him alone. I'll listen to their conversation. If she finds him not mad, send him to England or confine him somewhere else.

CLAUDIUS: It shall be so. Madness in great ones must not unwatched go.

(Polonius and Claudius exit.)

Act III
Scene 2

Setting: The great hall of Elsinore.

(Hamlet and three of the actors enter.)

HAMLET: Speak the speech as I gave it to you. Do not overdo it.

ACTOR: Yes, your honor.

HAMLET: Don't be too tame either. But let your own discretion be your tutor.

ACTOR: Yes, my lord.

(Actors exit.)

(Horatio enters.)

HORATIO: At your service, lord.

HAMLET: There is a play tonight before the king. One scene comes near the circumstances of my father's death. Observe my uncle to see if he hides guilt. I will keep my eyes on his face. After the play we will judge what we have seen. *(Trumpet sounds.)* They are coming! Get a place.

(Claudius, Gertrude, Polonius, Ophelia, Rosencrantz, Guildenstern, and other attendants enter.)

(The play begins. A king and queen enter. They are embracing in a loving fashion. He lies down to sleep. She leaves. Another man comes in and takes off the crown of the

sleeper. He then pours poison in the sleeper's ear and leaves. The queen returns to find the king dead. She cries loudly for the king. The poisoner comes to console the queen. He gives her many gifts. The two are married.)

(Actors exit.)

CLAUDIUS: *(Rising to his feet.)* Give me lights!

ATTENDANTS: Lights, lights, lights!

(All but Hamlet and Polonius exit.)

POLONIUS: My lord, the queen would like to speak with you.

HAMLET: Then I will come to my mother by and by.

(Polonius exits.) Let me be cruel. I will speak daggers to her, but use none.

(Hamlet exits.)

Act III
Scene 3

Setting: The king's private chapel.

(Claudius, Rosencrantz and Guildenstern enter.)

CLAUDIUS: It is not safe to let his madness rage. I command you to take him to England.

GUILDENSTERN: We will do as you ask.

ROSENCRANTZ: We will leave in haste.

(Rosencrantz and Guildenstern exit.)

CLAUDIUS: *(Kneeling.)* Oh, my offense is rank. It smells to heaven. A brother's murder is the oldest sin. What form of prayer can I say? 'Forgive my foul murder?' How can I ask forgiveness when I have the crown and the queen, for which I did commit murder? Oh wretched state! Help, angels!

(Hamlet enters.)

HAMLET: I could kill him easily now. But if I killed him while he was praying, his soul would go to heaven. A villain kills my father, and for that his son sends the villain to heaven? This would not be revenge. I will kill him when he is sinning. Drinking, gambling, or sleeping with my mother. And then his black soul will go to hell!

(Hamlet exits.)

CLAUDIUS: My words fly up. My thoughts remain below. Words without thoughts never go to heaven.

(Claudius exits.)

Act III
Scene 4

Setting: Gertrude's bedroom.

(Polonius and Gertrude enter.)

POLONIUS: Tell him that his pranks have been too much to bear. Be firm with him. I'll be behind the curtain.

(Polonius hides behind the curtains.)

(Hamlet enters.)

HAMLET: What's the matter, Mother?

GERTRUDE: Hamlet, thou hast thy father much offended.

HAMLET: Mother, you have my father much offended.

GERTRUDE: Come, come, you answer with an idle tongue.

HAMLET: Go, go, you question with a wicked tongue.

GERTRUDE: Have you forgotten who I am?

HAMLET: No, you are the queen, your husband's brother's wife. And I wish it were not so. You are my mother.

GERTRUDE: What are you going to do? Will thou murder me? Help! Help!

POLONIUS: *(Behind curtains.)* What? Help, help, help!

HAMLET: *(Drawing his sword.)* Is that a rat? *(Striking at the curtain.)* Dead for a gold coin!

POLONIUS: *(Behind curtains.)* Oh, I am slain!

GERTRUDE:	Oh, me, what a rash and bloody deed is this?
HAMLET:	A bloody deed? Almost as bad, good Mother, as kill a king and marry his brother.
GERTRUDE:	Kill a king?
HAMLET:	Those were my words. *(Draws curtains to reveal body of Polonius.)* Intruding fool, farewell.
GERTRUDE:	What have I done that you would speak to me like this?
HAMLET:	*(Holds up two small pictures, one of his father and one of Claudius.)* Look at these pictures. This was your husband. Here is your husband. Can your eyes tell them apart? You cannot call it love, for at your age the blood should be tame. Where is your shame?
GERTRUDE:	Oh, Hamlet, speak no more. Thou hast turned my eyes into my very soul. And there I see such black stains.
	(Ghost enters.)
GHOST:	Do not forget the purpose of your visit. Comfort your mother, Hamlet.
HAMLET:	Oh, Mother, look at him. How pale he is.
GERTRUDE:	To whom do you speak?
HAMLET:	Do you see nothing at all?
GERTRUDE:	Nothing at all.
HAMLET:	It is my father. Why look, he is now leaving through the door.
	(Ghost exits.)
GERTRUDE:	This is madness.
HAMLET:	Mother, for the love of grace, I am not mad.

Confess your sins. Repent what's past. Avoid what is to come.

GERTRUDE: Oh, Hamlet, thou hast cut my heart in two.

HAMLET: Throw away the worse part and live with the pure other half. Go not to my uncle's bed tonight. You will once again assume your virture. I do repent the death I gave tonight, but heaven hath made it so. I must be cruel only to be kind. Thus bad begins and worse remains. One word more, my lady.

GERTRUDE: What shall I do?

HAMLET: Do not explain that I am not really mad. And do not tell the king what I know. Your neck will be broken if that is done.

GERTRUDE: I will not breathe a word.

HAMLET: You know that I must go to England?

GERTRUDE: Alas, I had forgotten. Yes, it has been decided.

HAMLET: My two school friends whom I trust as much as fanged snakes have the orders. But I have other plans for them. *(Dragging body of Polonius.)* I'll lug the guts of this fool to another room. Come, sir, the end draws near. Good night, Mother.

(Hamlet exits dragging the body.)

Act IV
Scene 1

Setting: Gertrude's bedroom.

(Claudius enters.)

CLAUDIUS: Where is your son?

GERTRUDE: My lord, what I have seen tonight!

CLAUDIUS: What, Gertrude? How is Hamlet?

GERTRUDE: Mad as the sea and wind when both contend which is the mightier. Behind the curtains something stirs. He whips out his sword and cries 'a rat, a rat!' And he kills the good old man.

CLAUDIUS: Oh, heavy deed! His liberty is a threat to all. How shall this bloody deed be answered? Where has he gone?

GERTRUDE: To take the body he has killed. His madness shows itself pure. He now weeps for what he has done.

CLAUDIUS: Oh, Gertrude, we must ship him out of here before the sun sets on the mountains.

(Rosencrantz and Guildenstern enter.)

Friends, Hamlet in madness hath slain Polonius. From his mother's room, he hath dragged the body. Go and find it and bring it to the chapel.

(Rosencrantz and Guildenstern exit.)

We must call our wisest friends and let them know what has happened. Otherwise they may blame us for this. Oh, come away. My soul is full of discord and dismay.

(Claudius and Gertrude exit.)

Act IV
Scene 2

Setting: A hallway in the castle.

(Hamlet enters.)

HAMLET: Who calls on Hamlet? Oh, here they come.

(Rosencrantz and Guildenstern enter.)

ROSENCRANTZ: My lord, what have you done with the body?

HAMLET: It is with the dust that it is kin to.

ROSENCRANTZ: Tell us where it is that we may take it to the chapel.

HAMLET: Do not believe it.

ROSENCRANTZ: Believe what?

HAMLET: I cannot reply to a sponge.

ROSENCRANTZ: Do you take me for a sponge?

HAMLET: Ay, sir. You soak up the king's orders.

ROSENCRANTZ: I understand you not, my lord.

HAMLET: I'm glad of it.

ROSENCRANTZ: My lord, you must tell us where his body is.

HAMLET: The body is with the king. But the king is not with the body. The king is a thing.

GUILDENSTERN: A thing, my lord?

HAMLET: Of nothing. Bring me to him.

(All exit.)

Act IV
Scene 3

Setting: A stateroom in the castle.

(Claudius and attendants enter.)

CLAUDIUS: I have sent for him and the body. How dangerous it is that this man goes loose. Yet we must not punish him severely. He is too loved by the people. Sending him away is the answer.

(Rosencrantz enters.)

ROSENCRANTZ: We cannot get the body from him.

CLAUDIUS: But where is he?

ROSENCRANTZ: Guarded.

CLAUDIUS: Bring him before us.

ROSENCRANTZ: Bring in my lord!

(Guildenstern and Hamlet enter.)

CLAUDIUS: Now, Hamlet, where is Polonius?

HAMLET: At supper.

CLAUDIUS: At supper? Where?

HAMLET: Not where he eats, but is eaten. A certain group of worms is eating him.

CLAUDIUS: Where is Polonius?

HAMLET: In heaven. If you do not find him there, you shall see him in the lobby at the top of the stairs.

CLAUDIUS: Go see him there.

(Attendants exit.)

We grieve for what thou hast done. We must send you away with haste. Prepare yourself for England.

HAMLET: England?

CLAUDIUS: Ay, Hamlet.

HAMLET: For England! Farewell, dear mother.

CLAUDIUS: I am your father, Hamlet.

HAMLET: My mother. Father and mother is man and wife. Man and wife is one flesh. I leave for England.

(Hamlet exits.)

CLAUDIUS: Follow him. Make sure he leaves tonight. Everything is sealed and done. Make haste. *(Rosencrantz and Guildenstern exit.)* My letters will insure the present death of Hamlet. It will be done in England. He is like a fever in my blood. I must be cured. When I know it is done, my fortune will change.

Act IV
Scene 4

Setting: The sea coast near Elsinore.

(Young Fortinbras enters with army.)

FORTINBRAS: Captain, meet with the Danish king. Ask permission to march through his kingdom.

CAPTAIN: I will do it, my lord.

(Young Fortinbras exits with army.)

(Hamlet, Captain, Rosencrantz and Guildenstern enter.)

HAMLET: Good sir, whose army is this?

CAPTAIN: They are of Norway, sir.

HAMLET: What is their purpose here?

CAPTAIN: To attack Poland.

HAMLET: Who commands them?

CAPTAIN: The nephew to old Fortinbras.

HAMLET: What part of Poland will you attack?

CAPTAIN: A little patch of ground that hath no worth. It cannot even be farmed.

HAMLET: So many men shall die for little reason.

CAPTAIN: God be with you, sir.

(Captain exits.)

ROSENCRANTZ: Will it please you to go, my lord?

HAMLET: I'll be with you shortly. Go a little ahead.

(All but Hamlet exit.)

Here I stand with a father killed and a mother stained, when twenty thousand men go to death for a worthless plot of land. Where is my shame? From this time forth, my thoughts be bloody or they be worthless!

(Hamlet exits.)

Act IV
Scene 5

Setting: The great hall of the castle.

(Horatio, Gertrude, and an attendant enter.)

GERTRUDE: I will not speak with her.

ATTENDANT: She needs to be pitied.

HORATIO: You had better speak with her.

GERTRUDE: Let her come in.

(Attendant exits.)

(Ophelia enters.)

GERTRUDE: How are you, Ophelia?

OPHELIA: *(Singing.)*

> *He is dead and gone.*
> *He is dead and gone.*
> *At his head is grass.*
> *At his heels stone.*

(Claudius enters.)

GERTRUDE: Look, my lord.

OPHELIA: *(Singing.)*

> *Larded all with sweet flowers*
> *which to the grave did not go.*
> *With true love showers.*

CLAUDIUS:	How are you, pretty lady?
OPHELIA:	Lord, we know what we are, but know not what we may be.
CLAUDIUS:	Pretty Ophelia.
OPHELIA:	*(Singing.)*

You promised me to wed.
So would I had you not come to my bed.

CLAUDIUS:	How long has she been like this?
OPHELIA:	I hope all be well. But I cannot choose but to weep to think they would lay him in the cold ground. My brother shall know of this. Goodnight, goodnight.
	(Ophelia exits.)
CLAUDIUS:	Follow her closely. *(Horatio exits.)* Oh, Gertrude, when sorrow comes, it comes in bunches. Your son has gone. The people are angry about Polonius' death and his secret burial. Poor Ophelia has lost her senses. Her brother is on his way from France.
	(Messenger enters.)
CLAUDIUS:	What is the matter?
MESSENGER:	Young Laertes with a riotous mob is headed here. They cry 'We choose Laertes to be king! Laertes shall be king!'
	(Loud noise comes from outside.)
CLAUDIUS:	The doors have broken.
	(Laertes and crowd enter.)
LAERTES:	Vile King, give me my father!
CLAUDIUS:	Tell me, what is the cause of this? Why are

you so angry?

LAEERTES: Where is my father?

CLAUDIUS: Dead.

LAERTES: How did he die?

CLAUDIUS: I am guiltless of your father's death. But I grieve for him.

(Ophelia enters.)

OPHELIA: *(Singing.)*

> *They bore him bare faced on the bier.*
> *Hey non nonny, nonny, hey nonny---*
> *And in his grave rained many a tear.*
> *Fare you well, my dove.*

LAERTES: Where are your wits?

OPHELIA: There's rosemary. That's for remembrance. Pray you, love, remember. And there are pansies. That's for thoughts.

LAERTES: This is hell itself!

OPHELIA: No, no, he is dead. Go to thy death bed. He will never come again.

(Ophelia exits.)

LAERTES: Do you see this, God?

CLAUDIUS: Laertes, I share your grief. If you find we are involved in this, our kingdom is yours. But if not, we will work together to seek revenge.

LAERTES: Let this be so. His means of death and poor funeral must be questioned!

CLAUDIUS: And so it shall. And where the offense is, let the great axe fall.

(All exit.)

Act IV
Scene 6

Setting: A room in the castle.

(Horatio and attendant enter.)

HORATIO: Who are they?

ATTENDANT: Sailors, sir. They have letters for you.

HORATIO: Let them come in.

(Attendant exits.)

(Sailors enter.)

SAILOR: There is a letter for you, sir. It came from a gentleman who was bound for England.

HORATIO: *(Reads letter.)*

Horatio,

When you have read this, show these fellows to the king. They have letters for him. We were two days at sea when a pirate ship overtook us. I became their prisoner. They have brought me back and I must reward them.

These men are to bring you to me. I must tell you something that will surprise you greatly. Rosencrantz and Guildenstern are still heading for England. I have much to tell you of them.

Farewell,

Hamlet

Come. I will take you to the king. Then you may direct me to Hamlet.

(All exit.)

Act IV
Scene 7

Setting: A state room in the castle.

(Claudius and Laertes enter.)

CLADIUS: I am your friend, Laertes. He who hath slain your father also pursued my life.

LAERTES: Why did you not punish such a capital crime?

CLAUDIUS: There are two special reasons. The queen loves him dearly and I live for her. Also he is much admired by the people who have great affection for him.

LAERTES: And so I have a noble father lost and a sister driven to madness. But my revenge will come.

CLAUDIUS: Do not lose sleep for that. You must not think that this will be ignored. I loved your father.

(Messenger enters carrying letters.)

MESSENGER: My lord, letters from Hamlet. This one for you and this one for the queen.

(Messenger exits.)

CLAUDIUS: *(Reads letter.)*

High and mighty,

Tomorrow I shall return. First, I will ask your pardon. And then I will tell of my sudden and strange return.

Hamlet

What does this mean?

LAERTES: I do not know. But let him come!

CLAUDIUS: Will you do as I say?

LAERTES: Not if you want me to make peace with him.

CLAUDIUS: No, it will be a plan for his death. And everyone will think it is an accident.

LAERTES: Then I will do as you say.

CLAUDIUS: Revenge should have no bounds. When Hamlet has returned home, we will set up a duel between the two of you. He will not inspect the swords, so he will not see that yours has not been blunted. With a little shuffling, you will easily wound him.

LAERTES: I will do it. And for this purpose I will poison the tip of my sword. Where it touches, nothing can be saved. It will be death!

CLAUDIUS: Let's think further of this. If this plan should fail, we need a second plan. Let me see. I have it! When he becomes hot and dry from the fencing, he will call for a drink. I will have a cup with poison. If he isn't hit by your sword, he will be poisoned by the drink. What was that noise?

(Gertrude enters.)

GERTRUDE: One woe follows fast upon another's heel. Your sister's drowned, Laertes.

LAERTES: Drowned? Where?

GERTRUDE: There is a willow that grows by a brook. She was hanging flowers on the tree when the branch broke. She was pulled to a muddy death.

LAERTES: Too much water hast poor Ophelia. And therefore I forbid my tears. But I cannot stop nature. I had a speech of fire, but this news douses it.

(Laertes exits.)

CLAUDIUS: How much I had to do to calm his rage! Now I fear it will start again. Let's follow him.

(All exit.)

Act V
Scene 1

Setting: A graveyard near the castle.

(Two gravediggers enter.)

GRAVEDIGGER I: Is she to be given a Christian burial when she took her own life?

GRAVEDIGGER II: I tell you she is.

GRAVEDIGGER I: How can that be unless she drowned in self defense?

GRAVEDIGGER II: If this had not been a gentle woman, she would not have a Christian burial.

GRAVEDIGGER I: What's the use? Go get me some liquor. *(Sings.)*

> *In youth when I did love.*
>
> *Me thought it very sweet.*

(Gravedigger II exits.)

(Hamlet and Horatio enter.)

HAMLET: Has this fellow no feeling for his business? He sings while he is grave making.

HORATIO: He is so used to it, he doesn't even think about it.

GRAVEDIGGER I: *(Sings.)*

> *But age with his stealing steps*

Hath clawed me in his clutch.

(Throws up a skull.)

HAMLET: That skull once had a tongue in it and could sing. *(Picks up the skull.)* It might have been the skull of a man of the court. Now he's food for the worms.

GRAVEDIGGER I: *(Sings.)*

A pic axe and a spade,

a spade for a shrouding sheet.

(Throws up another skull.)

HAMLET: There's another. Why this may be the skull of a lawyer. Where are his cases and his tricks now? This fellow may have been a great buyer of land. Where is his land now? It will hardly fit in this box.

HORATIO: No, my lord.

HAMLET: Whose grave is this?

GRAVEDIGGER I: Someone who was a woman, but rest her soul, she's dead. *(Picking up another skull from the grave.)* Here's a skull now that hath been in the earth for three and twenty years.

HAMLET: Whose was it?

GRAVEDIGGER I: This was Yorick's skull, the king's jester.

HAMLET: Alas, poor Yorick! I knew him well. He was a fellow of infinite jest. He carried me on his back a thousand times. Where are your games, songs and tricks that used to set everyone roaring at the table? Here come the king, queen, and members of the court.

(A priest, King, Queen, Laertes, and a coffin

with attendants enter.)

LAERTES: What other ceremonies?

PRIEST: We have given her the rites that we can. Her death was doubtful. We were commanded to give her this funeral. She should have been put in unholy ground. Yet she is allowed to be buried here with flowers on her grave.

LAERTES: Can no more be done for her?

PRIEST: No more can be done for her.

LAERTES: Lay her in the earth. My sister will be an angel in heaven while you are in hell howling!

HAMLET: What? The fair Ophelia?

GERTRUDE: *(Scattering flowers on the grave.)* Sweets to the sweet. Farewell. I had hoped you would be Hamlet's wife. I thought I would decorate your bridal bed, not your grave.

LAERTES: I curse the head whose wicked deed deprived thee of thy wits. Hold off the earth till I have held her once more in my arms. *(Jumps into the grave.)*

HAMLET: *(Comes forward.)* Who is he to grieve so?

LAERTES: *(Climbing out of grave to lunge at Hamlet.)* The devil take thy soul!

HAMLET: Take your hands off my throat!

CLAUDIUS: Separate them! *(Attendants part them.)*

HAMLET: I loved Ophelia. Forty thousand brothers could not with all their love equal mine!

CLAUDIUS: Laertes, he is mad.

GERTRUDE: For the love of God, leave him alone.

HAMLET: Have you come here to whine and outdo me

117

by leaping into the grave? Be buried with her and so will I. Let them throw a mountain of earth on us. I can rant as well as you!

(Hamlet exits.)

CLAUDIUS: Good Horatio, look after him.

(Horatio exits.)

(Aside to Laertes.) Strengthen your patience. Remember our discussion. We will take care of this matter. Gertrude, set watch over your son.

(All exit.)

Act V
Scene 2

Setting: The great hall of the castle.

(Hamlet and Horatio enter.)

HAMLET: I couldn't sleep. I left my cabin and went into their cabin. I stole their letters and took them to my room. I opened the official papers from the king. In them, I found an order to cut off my head. The reason given was for the safety of Denmark and England. Would you like to hear how I did proceed?

HORATIO: Please tell me.

HAMLET: I sat down and wrote a new set of orders. I made a plea that he should put the bearer of this letter to sudden death.

HORATIO: How did you seal the new orders?

HAMLET: I had my father's ring with me. I placed the new orders in the letter and then sealed it. The change was never known. The next day was the sea battle. You already know about that.

HORATIO: So Rosencrantz and Guildenstern went to their deaths?

HAMLET: They are not on my conscience. This is their own fault. They were making themselves useful to the king.

HORATIO: The king will soon hear from the King of

England.

HAMLET: Very shortly. I am very sorry that I forgot myself with Laertes. His bravery in grief made me angry.

(Osric enters.)

OSRIC: Welcome back to Denmark, lord.

HAMLET: Thank you.

OSRIC: I have a message from His Majesty.

HAMLET: I will receive it, sir.

OSRIC: The king asked me to tell you that he has made a wager on you. He has wagered that in a dozen bouts, Laertes will not win three more than you. Laertes said he would win nine out of the twelve. What is your answer?

HAMLET: Let the swords be brought. If the king is still of this purpose, I will win for him if I can. If not, I will gain nothing but my shame.

OSRIC: Very well, your lordship.

(Osric exits.)

HORATIO: You will lose this wager, my lord.

HAMLET: I do not think so. Since he went to France, I have been in continual practice. I shall win. I feel uneasy about this, but it is no matter.

HORATIO: If your mind is telling you something, obey it. I will tell them you are not well.

HAMLET: No, there is a special providence in the fall of the sparrow. Being ready is the important thing. Let it be.

(Claudius, Gertrude, Hamlet, Laertes, Osric, and attendants enter. The table is prepared

with wine and fruit; soldiers with trumpets and drums stand by. Laertes and Hamlet shake hands.)

HAMLET: Give me your pardon, sir. I have done you wrong. But pardon me as you are a gentleman. Was it Hamlet who wronged Laertes? Hamlet denies it. Who then? His madness. His madness is poor Hamlet's enemy. Sir, in front of this audience, please forgive me.

LAERTES: I am satisfied. I will not reconcile until later. But till that time I do receive your love and will not turn away from you.

HAMLET: I embrace you. Give us the swords.

CLAUDIUS: Give them the swords! Hamlet, you know the wager?

HAMLET: Very well, my lord. Your grace has laid odds on the weaker side.

LAERTES: This sword is too heavy. Let me see another.

HAMLET: The swords are all the same length?

OSRIC: Ay, my lord.

(They prepare to fence.)

CLAUDIUS: Set out the wine. If Hamlet wins the first or second hit, the king will drink to his success. And he shall throw a pearl into the cup. Give me the cups. Come, begin. Judges keep a close eye.

(They fence.)

HAMLET: One hit!

LAERTES: No.

HAMLET: Judgement?

OSRIC: A definite hit.

CLAUDIUS:	Hamlet, this pearl is thine. Here's to thy health.
	(Drums roll and trumpets sound.)
HAMLET:	I'll play this bout first. Set it aside.
	(They fence again.) Another hit! What say you?
LAERTES:	A touch, a touch. I do confess.
CLAUDIUS:	Our son shall win.
GERTRUDE:	The queen drinks to your fortune, Hamlet. *(Raises cup to her lips)*
CLAUDIUS:	Gertrude, do not drink!
GERTRUDE:	I will, my lord. I pray you pardon me.
	(Gertrude drinks and offers cup to Hamlet.)
CLAUDIUS:	*(Aside.)* It is the poisoned cup. It is too late.
HAMLET:	I dare not drink yet.
GERTRUDE:	Come, let me wipe your face.
LAERTES:	*(Aside.)* My lord, I'll hit him now.
CLAUDIUS:	I do not think so.
LAERTES:	*(Aside.)* And yet, it is almost against my conscience.
HAMLET:	Come, this is the third bout. Give me your best violence!
LAERTES:	So you say? Come on.
	(Laertes wounds Hamlet; scuffling, they exchange swords.)
CLAUDIUS:	Part them.
HAMLET:	Come again.
	(Hamlet wounds Laertes. Gertrude falls.)
GERTRUDE:	Oh, my dear Hamlet! The drink, the drink! I am poisoned. *(She dies.)*

HAMLET:	Who did this? Let the door be locked.
LAERTES:	Hamlet, you are dying, too. No medicine in the world can cure thee. In less than half an hour we will both be done. The foul practice has turned itself on me. Here I lie never to rise again. Thy mother's poisoned. I can say no more. The king is to blame.
HAMLET:	The sword point poisoned, too? Then poison do thy work.
	(Hamlet stabs the king with the sword.)
CLAUDIUS:	Defend me, friends. I am hurt.
HAMLET:	Drink the rest of the poison, you murderous Dane. Follow my mother.
LAERTES:	He is justly served. Exchange forgiveness with me, noble Hamlet. My death and my father's death are not upon you. And your death is not upon me. *(Dies.)*
HAMLET:	I am dead, Horatio
HORATIO:	There's still some poison left. *(Lifts cup to drink.)*
HAMLET:	Give me the cup. *(He grabs it from Horatio.)* Horatio, what a wounded name I would leave behind if you do not stay to tell my story.
	(Shots and marching sounds heard in the distance.)
	What battle is that?
OSRIC:	Young Fortinbras has returned from his victory in Poland.
HAMLET:	I cannot stay alive to see him. But I predict that Fortinbras will be the new King of Denmark. He has my dying support. So tell him about the events here. The rest is

silence.

HORATIO: Good night, sweet Prince. Flights of angels sing thee to thy rest!

(Young Fortinbras and soliders enter.)

FORTINBRAS: What is this?

HORATIO: I shall tell you everything. So you shall hear of bloody and unnatural acts. You will hear of accidents and murders. You will hear all this and more.

FORTINBRAS: Then let us call everyone together to hear this. It is with much sorrow that I embrace my fortune. For this is my kingdom now.

HORATIO: I shall speak of that, too.

FORTINBRAS: Let four captains bear Hamlet like a soldier to the stage. For he would have proved himself to be most royal. And for his passage, soldier's music and rites of war shall speak loudly for him.

(Soldiers carry Hamlet's body; drums and cannons are heard in the distance.)

THE GLOBE THEATER

The Globe Theater may well be the most famous theater in the world, for it was here that Shakespeare and other literary giants of his day produced their plays and other dramatic works.

Shakespeare and several other well-known actors needed a place to perform and so they pooled their funds and designed and built the Globe in 1599. Since they were theatrical professionals in every sense of the word, the building fit their needs perfectly. The Globe was octagonally-shaped with a roofless inner pit into which the stage projected. Three galleries (balconies) rose one above the other, the topmost of which had a thatched roof. One day, in order to provide reality in a production of Shakespeare's *King Henry the Eighth*, a cannon was discharged. Unfortunately, this piece of stagecraft set fire to the thatched roof, and the entire building burned. It was rebuilt the following year but was torn down 30 years later by the Puritans, who needed the space for houses.

A new Globe Theater was recently completed in London. Only materials that would have been found in the original Globe were used – a perfect setting to enjoy Shakespeare's genius.

About the Editors

Peggy L. Anderson, PhD, is a professor and Special Education Program Coordinator at Metropolitan State College of Denver. She has taught students with learning disabilities at the elementary and middle school levels in South Carolina and Florida. Her master's degree is from the Citadel and her doctorate is from the University of Denver. She completed her postdoctoral work with the Department of Pediatrics at Johns Hopkins University. Her research interests have focused on language-learning disabilities, dyslexia, and inclusion issues.

Judith D. Anderson, JD, is a trial attorney in southern California, specializing in the defense of school districts. She has taught Shakespeare to high school students in the United States and the United Kingdom for ten years. As a Fullbright Scholar, she travelled extensively in the British Isles, and met with the Queen Mother of England. She received her bachelor's degree at Flagler College and her law degree at Southwestern University School of Law.